# TRANSITIONS:

Decision-Making
in a
World of Change

# TRANSITIONS:

## Decision-Making in a World of Change

### STUDENT BOOK

Rev. Michael A. Librandi
Christopher R. Weickert

**TEL Publishers, Ltd.**
Rockford, IL

Photo Credits

The photographs reproduced in this text are from the following sources:

Rockford Diocesan Youth Ministry Office
Young Life Office of Rockford
Mark Blassage
Michael Librandi
Christopher Weickert
Perry Hunter
Laura Laughlin

---

**Nihil Obstat:**
**Thomas G. Doran**
**Censor Deputatus**

**Imprimatur:**
**†Arthur J. O'Neill**
**Bishop of Rockford**
**July 17, 1986**

The Nihil Obstat and Imprimatur are official declarations that a book or pamphlet is free of doctrinal or moral error. No implication is contained therein that those who have granted the Nihil Obstat and Imprimatur agree with the contents, opinions or statements expressed.

Copyright © 1986 by TEL Publishers, Ltd. All rights reserved.
No part of this book may be reproduced or transmitted in any form or by any means, electronic or mechanical, including photocopying, recording or by any information storage and retrieval system, without permission in writing from the Publisher, TEL Publishers, Ltd., P.O. Box 5471, Rockford, Illinois 61125.

ISBN 1-55588-127-0

Copyright © 1986 by TEL Publishers, Ltd.
P.O. Box 5471   Rockford, Illinois 61125
All rights reserved

Printed in the United States of America

## Contents

1. **Direction for Life** .................. 1
   Education
   Spiritual Growth
   Ministry

2. **Leadership** ...................... 25
   Education
   Spiritual Growth
   Ministry

3. **Commitments** ................... 49
   Education
   Spiritual Growth
   Ministry

4. **Fear of Failure** .................. 71
   Education
   Spiritual Growth
   Ministry

5. **Peer Pressure** ................... 99
   Education
   Spiritual Growth
   Ministry

6. **Moral Decisions, Part 1** .......... 123
   Education
   Spiritual Growth
   Ministry

7. **Moral Decisions, Part 2** .......... 139
   Education
   Spiritual Growth
   Ministry

8. **Wholeness** ..................... 161
   Education
   Spiritual Growth
   Ministry

## Chapter 1

**Direction for Life**

# VALUE SYSTEM ACTIVITY

**Discussion Questions**

A. What is your favorite room in your house? WHY?

B. What is your favorite time of day? WHY?

C. If you could take a trip anywhere in the world, where would you go? WHY?

D. If you had one million dollars tax free, what would you do with it? WHY?

E. If you could change one thing in your church, what would it be? WHY?

F. If you could ask God one question, what would you ask? WHY?

G. Do you consider yourself a Christian? WHY?

## STAGES OF DEVELOPMENT

We can divide various value systems into four general categories and look at these categories as developmental. In other words, the direction for life (the motives behind why a person acts in a certain way) can be seen as stages in our growth as human beings. We are going to name these four stages:
1) Challenger, 2) Searcher, 3) Traditionalist, and 4) Synthesizer.

**NOTES:**

### Stage one—THE CHALLENGER

Characteristics include:

_____

_____

_____

_____

_____

### Stage two—THE SEARCHER

Characteristics include:

_____

_____

_____

_____

_____

### Stage three—THE TRADITIONALIST

Characteristics include:

_____

_____

_____

_____

_____

### Stage four—THE SYNTHESIZER

Characteristics include:

_____

_____

_____

_____

_____

# THE CHURCH'S VALUE SYSTEM

## Summary

The Biblical Patriarchs — Abraham for example — allowed their values to be influenced by their faith and trust in God. You know the story of Abraham. He had a religious experience and sensed that he was called by God to move to a different land which would eventually become the kingdom of Israel. Abraham had to step out in faith. He had no assurance of success in taking the land away from its inhabitants. Abraham believed that his God would be with him in this venture. All the stories in the bible about Abraham emphasize his faith and trust in God. Abraham got his direction for life from his faith and trust in God.

Isaac, Abraham's son and another one of the Patriarchs, again had great faith and trust in God. The bible stories about Isaac consistently show how his life was led by his faith and trust in God.

Isaac's son, Jacob, had his name changed to Israel, the Hebrew word which means 'He fought with God'. Jacob, just like all of us, wanted to do things his own way. The bible stories about Jacob indicate that when we try to do things on our own without God's help we get into trouble. Things seem to go a lot better when we are living in faith and trust God.

The founding fathers of the Jewish faith (the Patriarchs) knew that faith and trust in God was the single most important element of success. Without faith and trust in their God they were nothing. It was their faith that gave them life. It seems that for them, direction in life came directly from their relationship with God.

Isn't that also the message of the Christian scriptures, the New Testament? The key to happiness according to Jesus is faith and trust in God. The key to new life is faith and trust in God. That seems to be what's behind many of the cure stories in the gospels. Someone wants to be cured from an affliction which is keeping him/her from living life to its fullest—like being blind or lame or deaf or mute. When they are cured Jesus points out that it was their faith and trust in God that cured them and because of that faith and trust in God they are now able to participate in a new life of happiness.

Maybe the point the gospels are trying to make is that our key to happiness in life is directly related to our relationship of faith and trust in God.

Sounds easy doesn't it? All we have to do is trust in God and have faith. Well if it were so easy all our troubles would have been over long ago. Maybe complete faith and trust in God represents stage five of our value system construct. It's the stage that comes after the Synthesizer. We could call it the Contemplative Stage. That's the stage where a person's mind and heart are in union with God. They are one with God in the sense that their whole person takes seriously and regards as possible Jesus' directive to love God with all your self and to love your neighbor as yourself.

Sounds a lot like it takes an angel to be living that value system all the time. It's what the church teaches us to value in life. The trouble is most of us are not even to the synthesizer stage, let alone the contemplative stage. Does that mean we can't take some direction for life from the value system of the church?

I bet you knew the answer would be, "Of course it doesn't!" After all, this is a religious education class! In basketball, for example, the goal of any player is to sink every shot he/she attempts. But is that what happens in reality? Of course not! Just because it doesn't happen in every game, does that mean the great player rejects it as a goal? An artist strives to create beautiful art objects, yet every attempt is not a masterpiece!

In baseball, a player with a 400 batting average would be considered great. But that also means that in six out of every ten tries at hitting the ball he/she fails! A great player is never discouraged by the misses—the goal is still to hit the ball every time.

All people need a direction for life. It's natural to want a full and a happy life. As followers of Jesus Christ we are called to seek perfect happiness in our relationship with each other and with God. That means working out of a value system that says complete faith and trust in God is necessary and yes—even possible. That means trusting in God even when it's not popular at the time: you know, when someone does something to hurt you and the voice of the world says "Get em" while the voice of God says "Forgive, forget and believe." Sometimes we fall short of the goal. God continues to love us and urge us on. Go for it!

Date: 12/2/3010

## SAMPLE ANALYSIS SHEET

Analyze each of the objects in your samples. Write what you think it is and how it was used by the people who formed it. Divide the samples up among the group.

_____

_____

_____

_____

_____

_____

_____

_____

_____

_____

_____

_____

_____

_____

# SAMPLE ANALYSIS SHEET (CONTINUED)

## DESCRIPTION OF SOCIETY

This is your thesis on the society which you have been examining. Please describe the culture in as much detail as possible. Support your description with artifacts.

_____

_____

_____

_____

_____

_____

_____

_____

_____

_____

_____

_____

_____

_____

_____

_____

_____

## DESCRIPTION OF SOCIETY (CONTINUED)

**Acts 2:42-47**
"They devoted themselves to the apostles' instruction and the communal life, to the breaking of bread and the prayers. A reverent fear overtook them all, for many wonders and signs were performed by the apostles. Those who believed shared all things in common; they would sell their property and goods, dividing everything on the basis of each one's need. They went to the temple area every day, while in their homes they broke bread. With exultant and sincere hearts they took their meals in common, praising God and winning the approval of all the people. Day by day the Lord added to their number those who were being saved."

## JOURNALING—DIRECTION FOR LIFE

Remember to:
1. Focus on your feelings about an idea.
2. Write for yourself, not as if someone else is going to read it.
3. Write honestly. Say what you really feel, not what you think you are supposed to feel.
4. Don't go back and erase thoughts. Clarify them if you have to, but don't erase them.
5. Be open and creative. See what you can come up with."

Try to answer one or both of the following questions.

What is my direction for life?

How compatible is my direction for life with the direction for life of the early Christians?

## JOURNALING (CONTINUED)

_____
_____
_____
_____
_____
_____
_____
_____
_____
_____
_____
_____
_____

## JOURNALING (CONTINUED)

## PRAYER—DIRECTION FOR LIFE

**ALL:** In the name of the Father, and of the Son and of the Holy Spirit.

**TEACHER:** Dear God, thank you for all you have given us. Today we have looked at our directions for life. You know what lies in the heart of each of us, where we find joy, what we seek from life. Help us to grow in our understanding of you and your love for us.

**A:** We are all so different.

**B:** Yet so alike.

**A:** We come from many backgrounds.

**B:** Yet are children of the one God.

**A:** We search for meaning in many directions.

**B:** Yet it rests before us in your word.

**ALL:** Help us to recognize the gifts you set before us. Guide us so we may follow you faithfully.

**READER 1:** (Matthew 4:18-22 paraphrased)
"As Jesus was walking along the sea of Galilee he watched two brothers, Simon now known as Peter and his brother Andrew, casting a net into the sea. They were fishermen. Jesus said to them, 'Come after me and I will make you fishers of men.' Simon and Andrew immediately abandoned their nets and became his followers. Jesus walked along further and caught sight of two other brothers, James and John. They too were in their boat, getting their nets in order with their father Zebedee. Jesus called them, and immediately they abandoned their boat and their father to follow him."

**TEACHER:** Often we are too busy to hear the call of God in our lives. We clutter life doing so many things we seldom take time to hear, let alone act on God's direction for our lives.

**A:** If I knew what I should do, of course I would do it.

**B:** If I had the time I would help people more.

**A:** If only other people would begin to do it, then I could do it more easily.

**B:** If I didn't have a job, or practice, or so much homework, I might have more time to pray.

**A:** If church wasn't so boring I would be more active.

**ALL:** If only . . .

**READER 2:** (Matthew 6:19-21 paraphrased)
"Do not store up for yourself earthly treasures. Moths and rust corrode; thieves break in and steal. Make it your practice instead to store up heavenly treasure, which neither moths nor rust corrode or thieves break in and steal. Remember, where your treasure is, there your heart is also."

(pause)

**ALL:** Holy Spirit, help us find our direction for life. There are so many choices to make we may loose ourselves on the way. Give us courage to seek after the lasting joys of your Spirit rather than the fleeting joys of the world. As we choose our direction for life, help us to keep in mind the treasure of your love. Guide us, for we often make mistakes. Teach us to follow you as we pray the words your son taught his friends.

Our Father . . . (pray the Our Father)

## OUTLINE OF MINISTRY MODULE

A. C1—DIRECTION FOR LIFE
   1. Peer ministry outline
   2. Qualities of ministry
   3. Explanation of ministry

B. C2—LEADERSHIP
   1. Skills for ministry
      a. Leadership skills
      b. Group dynamics
   2. Results of ministry

C. C3—COMMITMENTS
   1. Skills of ministry
      a. Communication
      b. Listening
   2. Limits in ministry

D. C4—FEAR OF FAILURE
   1. Ministerial situations
      a. Cries for help
      b. Suicide and Depression
      c. Confidences

E. C5—PEER PRESSURE
   1. Ministerial situations
      a. Alcohol and drugs

F. C6—EVANGELIZATION
   1. Ministerial situations
      a. Communication with parents

G. C7—CALL TO MINISTRY
   1. Ministerial situations
      a. Break-ups and reconciliation
      b. Peer pressure
      c. Rumors

H. C8—OTHER RELIGIONS
   1. Complete ministry

## NOW WHO?

1. Someone offers to pay you if you will do his/her homework. You say you don't know and will tell the person tomorrow. Now who would you talk to?

   _____

2. The guy/girl you have been dating says he/she wants to have sex with you. You really like this person but he/she has a reputation for using people and then dropping them. You have a date at the end of the week and he/she expects you to have an answer then. Now who would you talk to?

   _____

   If that person was not around, then who?

   _____

3. You get an "A" on a paper that you really worked hard on. Now who would you talk to?

   _____

4. Someone offers you a job in a store that would pay you more than you are making. You already have a job and they really depend on you at work. Now who would you talk to?

_____

5. Someone in your class you don't like much is accused of stealing the answer key for an upcoming test. She is suspended for a week. Later that day you see the answer key in the folder of one of your best friends. You know his parents would be really mad if he was suspended. Now who would you talk to?

_____

6. You are in line at a checkout counter and you overhear someone talking about a girl who recently left your school. They are saying that she left because she was pregnant, not because her family was going to move. Now who would you talk to if she had been dating your brother?

_____

7. You can't decide whether to try out for a sport at school. Now who would you talk to?

_____

8. You find a wallet in the park and call the owner of it to tell him you found it. He is very grateful and says you can keep the money it contains. There is about $50 in the wallet, but the owner says it is okay to keep it. Now who would you talk to?

_____

9. You are sitting outside and you watch an absolutely beautiful sunset. Now who would you talk to?

_____

1. _____

2. _____

3. _____

4. _____

5. _____

**Definition of Ministry:** "Ministry is finding within yourself the ability to openly, honestly, and compassionately care for other people. Growing from your individual response to the bountiful love of God it is the natural tendency to hope for better in the world and work to make it happen. Ministry is what you have been doing your whole life whenever you reached out to another human being in an effort to improve the condition of their world, which in turn witnesses hope for the world as a whole."

## "QUALITIES OF A FRIEND"

What do you consider the qualities of a "good friend"? People have many acquaintances in their lifetime but few people ever become our good friends. What are the qualities which make someone your good friend?

_____

_____

_____

_____

_____

_____

_____

_____

_____

_____

_____

_____

_____

## QUALITIES OF A MINISTER

1. _____
2. _____
3. _____
4. _____
5. _____
6. _____
7. _____
8. _____
9. _____
10. _____

Term _____
Definition:

_____

_____

_____

_____


Term _____
Definition:

_____

_____

_____

_____

**Leadership**

*Chapter*
**2**

## WHAT IS LEADERSHIP?

**NOTES:**

## SATISFACTION SCALE

GROUP _____
Were you the leader? \_\_\_\_ YES \_\_\_\_ NO

On a scale of 1 to 10 (1 is low, 10 is perfect) rate your experience:

1. My satisfaction with the leader \_\_\_\_

2. My satisfaction with my own participation \_\_\_\_

3. My satisfaction with the group's product \_\_\_\_

**NOTES:**

DICTATOR STYLE:




LAISSEZ-FAIRE STYLE:




CONSENSUS STYLE:

## MOSES IS CALLED TO LEADERSHIP

**Exodus 3:1-15 and 4:1-17 (paraphrased)**

One day as Moses was tending the flock of his father-in-law Jethro out at the edge of the desert near Horeb, the mountain of God, the angel of God appeared to him as a flame of fire in a bush. When Moses saw that the bush was on fire and that it didn't burn up, he went over to investigate.

Then God called out to him, "Moses, Moses!" "Who is it?" Moses asked. "Don't come any closer," God said, "Take off your shoes because you are in a holy place. I am the God of your fathers—the God of Abraham, Isaac, and Jacob."

Then God told him, "I have seen the deep trouble and pain of my people in Egypt, and have heard their cry for freedom from their forced hard work. I have come to deliver them from the Egyptians and to take them out of Egypt into a good land of their very own. Yes the cry of the people of Israel has risen to me in heaven, and I have seen the heavy tasks the Egyptians have oppressed them with. Now I am going to send you to Pharaoh, to demand that he let you lead my people out of Egypt."

"But I'm not the person for a job like that!" Moses said. God told him, "I will be with you and help you."

Then Moses asked, "If I go to the people of Israel and tell them that their father's God has sent me, they will ask, 'Which God are you talking about?' What will I tell them then?"

"Just tell them that I AM WHO I AM sent you," God answered. "Tell them the God of their fathers, the God of Abraham, Isaac and Jacob sent you. Tell them the Lord God sent you."

But Moses said, "They won't believe me! They won't do what I tell them to. They'll say, 'God never appeared to you!'"

"What do you have in your hand?" God asked him.

"A shepherd's staff," Moses answered.

Then God said, "Throw it down on the ground." So Moses threw his shepherd's staff down to the ground and it instantly became a snake and Moses jumped back away from it.

God said, "Grab it by the tail and pick it up." Moses did and it immediately became a shepherd's staff again.

"Do that and they'll believe you!" said God. "Do that and they'll believe that the God of Abraham, Isaac and Jacob sent you! Now reach into your robe and put your hand next to your chest." Moses did and when he took it out again his hand was white and covered with leprosy! "Now put your hand back inside your robe," God said. Moses did and when he took it out again it was cured and back to normal.

"If they don't believe you after the snake miracle, use this one and they will have to believe. Just in case they are still doubting you, here's one more thing you can do. Take some water from the Nile River and pour it on the dry ground. As you pour it on the ground it will turn to blood."

But Moses pleaded, "Lord, I'm really quite shy. I've never been very good at speaking and I'm still not good at speaking. In fact I have a speech impediment." "Who created mouths?" asked God. "Is it not I who make people who can speak or not speak, see or not see, hear or not hear? Now go and do what I am telling you to do. Do not be afraid. I will be with you and help you find the right words to speak."

But Moses was really afraid of all this so he tried one more time, "Lord, please send someone else-anyone but me!" Then God got a little impatient with Moses and said, "Look, you have a brother don't you. Take Aaron with you and he can be your mouthpiece. He's a good speaker, tell him what to say and let him do the talking. Just get moving on this. And be sure to take your shepherd's staff along."

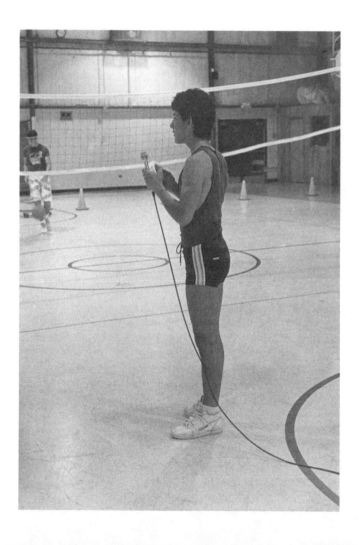

## MOSES' PERSONAL PROFILE

**Notes:**

## Leadership Conclusions

Moses is considered the great leader of the Hebrew people in the Old Testament. Yet from the description of Moses' call to leadership we can see that he was not always sure of himself. He didn't think he could do the job God called him to do.

God calls all of us to leadership, but not always in the sense of being a leader like Moses or being the lead in one of your school plays or even being in charge of some great project. Leadership doesn't only refer to being the president of the student council. Leadership refers to anyone who has an opportunity in daily life to influence another person by his/her behavior, attitudes and values.

Anyone can be a leader in that sense and everyone is called to leadership. Have you ever been talking with a group of friends when one person started putting down someone you all know? Sometimes no one says anything positive about the person being criticized for fear of disagreeing with the speaker. Later you find out a lot of your friends disagreed with what was being said but no one had the courage to speak up. One person can really change the whole opinion of a group.

Why was Moses afraid to become the leader God wanted him to be? I suppose it was because he knew he would have to deal with peer pressure. I'm sure Moses was afraid of not being liked. He was shy and thought someone else could do a better job. Moses needed some confidence and some help from his brother, Aaron. Moses shared his leadership with Aaron and together they created positive peer pressure which eventually freed a whole population.

Have you ever thought about the positive peer pressure you can create with shared leadership among your friends? Your leadership can free people too. Your leadership can free people from the fear of rejection we all feel at times. Your shared leadership can free people to love themselves, love others and even to love God. What is your leadership style? Think about it.

# DOROTHY DAY

Born in Brooklyn, New York, in 1897, Dorothy Day focused her leadership on promoting awareness of the needs of the poor and homeless. She not only spoke and wrote about this, but she co-founded the Catholic Worker Movement which continues today.

Dorothy Day was not born a Catholic. In fact, she did not become a Catholic until she was 30 years old. Living for a time in San francisco, she commented on the warm spirit and charity which she saw after the San Francisco earthquake and fire. After moving to Chicago Dorothy looked for a community which shared her concern for others. She was appalled at the "ugliness of life in a world which professed to be Christian. . ." She felt her faith had nothing in common with that of the Christians around her, so she joined the Socialist party. At this time she had not yet become a Catholic.

She moved from her parents' house and lived in an unheated New York tenement. She worked for five dollars a week and wrote a column about the horrible conditions in the slums.

After considering becoming a Catholic for several years, Dorothy Day was baptized in December of 1927. One of the factors she said led her to consider the Catholic Church was seeing people go to early weekday Mass. Something about the faith of the people attending drew her to want to share in that faith.

In 1932 she met Peter Maurin. He proved very instrumental in her education as a Catholic, bringing her articles and books to read. The two of them created a newspaper called 'The Catholic Worker.' The object of this eight-page paper was, 'to popularize and make known the encyclicals of the popes in regard to social justice.' It also served as an instrument to address social problems such as labor issues and race relations. Eventually people began to

go to the newspaper office looking for food and shelter.

As a response to this need, a house of hospitality was founded. This was the first of over thirty such houses that would be founded for the poor.

Dorothy Day voluntarily lived in poverty until her death, speaking out for the rights of all individuals to be free from hunger and free from unnecessary suffering.

## RISK LIST

I would be willing to . . . if necessary to improve my relationship with God.

_____ Lose some of my friends . . .

_____ Change where I lived . . .

_____ Live in a slum . . .

_____ Sell my stereo, radio, records etc. . . .

_____ Not learn to drive . . .

_____ Risk being laughed at . . .

_____ Say what I believe even when it is not the most popular thing . . .

_____ Attend Sunday Mass . . .

_____ Attend weekday Mass . . .

_____ Work for little pay . . .

_____ Work for no pay . . .

_____ Work with people very different than myself . . .

_____ Not have a closet full of clothes . . .

_____ Put God first in my life . . .

_____ Volunteer my time at church . . .

_____ Do things differently than others . . .

## JOURNALING—LEADERSHIP

> Henry Steele Commanger—"We believe that our words—which we assume to express our principles—represent us more than our actions, but to outsiders it is the actions that are more eloquent than the words."

Write a reaction to this statement.

_____

_____

_____

_____

_____

_____

_____

_____

_____

_____

_____

_____

_____

## JOURNALING (CONTINUED)

## JOURNALING (CONTINUED)

_____
_____
_____
_____
_____
_____
_____
_____

## PRAYER—LEADERSHIP

**ALL:** In the name of the Father and of the Son and of the Holy Spirit.

**TEACHER:** Merciful God, there are many times our words and our actions don't match. We say we are followers of Christ yet we ignore those in need around us. Help us to live your teachings.

**A:** A reading from the Gospel of John.

**B:** "As God has loved me so I have loved you. Live on in my love."

**A:** "You will live in my love if you keep my commandments, even as I have kept God's commandments, and live in God's love."

**B:** "All this I tell you that my joy may be yours and your joy may be complete.

**ALL:** "This is my commandment: love one another as I have loved you. There is no greater love than this: to lay down one's life for one's friends."

**A:** "You are my friends if you do what I have commanded you. I no longer speak of you as slaves, for a slave does not know what the master is about. Instead I call you friends, since I have made known to you all that I heard from God."

**B:** "It was not you who chose me, it was I who chose you to go forth and bear fruit. Your fruit must endure, so that all you ask of God in my name will be given to you."

**ALL:** "The commandment I give you is this, that you love one another."

**TEACHER:** The words are easy to say, but they are difficult to live. Give us the courage to take risks in

our lives so that we can make our actions and our words one and the same. St. Francis asked in prayer similar things to the ones which we pray for today. I would ask that you would bless us as we pray the Prayer of St. Francis.

**ALL:** Lord, make me an instrument of your peace; Where there is hatred, let me sow love; Where there is despair, hope; Where there is darkness, light; and where there is sadness, joy. O Divine Master, grant that I may not so much seek to be consoled, as to console; to be understood, as to understand; to be loved, as to love; for it is in giving that we receive, it is in pardoning that we are pardoned, and it is dying that we are born to eternal life.

**TEACHER:** It was once said that, "what lies before us and what lies behind us are tiny matters next to what lies within us." Dear God we pray that you would be with us, and within us, for we want our hearts to follow that which is good. Help us to follow your teachings that in our lives we too may be leaders.

**ALL:** (Pray the "Our Father")

## LEADERSHIP

**Formal Power:** The power or influence held by the "official" leadership of a group

**Informal Power:** The power or influence held by the "un-official" leadership within a group

**Group norms:** The unwritten rules of conduct which govern the behaviors of individuals within a group.

**Nonconformist:** An individual who does not abide by the group norms

**Anti-conformist:** An individual who does the opposite of what is dictated by the norms of the group

**Independence:** Acting in a way which deviates from the group norm because of a belief that other behaviors are correct

# ROLES OF A LEADER

A. Mrs. Schmidt is a member of the parish council. Three months ago the parish decided to install a wheelchair ramp to provide access to the church for parishioners confined to wheelchairs. The project was turned over to a committee which Mrs. schmidt heads. After much discussion the committee decided how the ramp would be put together. Mr. Bean said he would take care of it. Today the pastor called Mrs. Schmidt. He was unhappy, and he said that if the ramp was not in by the end of the week he would hire a carpenter to do the job. What three things should Mrs. Schmidt do?

B. Steve just went to a meeting sponsored by a group called S.A.D.D. (Students Against Drunk Driving). He was really impressed by some of the ideas he heard. The members were not square and stupid as he thought they might be. Since Steve's school is close to a state where the drinking age is 18 while the age in his state is 21, most of his classmates drive to bars in the other state. Then they drive home drunk. Last year two students at his school were killed while driving home drunk. Steve would like to try to start a chapter of S.A.D.D. at his school. What three things should Steve do?

C. Donna is very popular and has many friends. She would not want to do anything that would risk her relationship with her friends. Two weeks ago a new girl, Lisa, came to school. She is paralyzed from an accident in which she was hit by a car driven by a drunk driver. Donna found herself sitting with Lisa in the main office one day before school. Donna found that Lisa had a good sense of humor and that they shared some interests. When Donna arrived at school one day, she saw that while Lisa was looking away, some of the other girls put Lisa's books on a ledge where she couldn't reach them. Then the girls were ignoring Lisa and whispering among themselves. They are some of Donna's best friends. What three things should Donna do?

_____
_____
_____
_____
_____
_____
_____
_____
_____
_____
_____
_____
_____
_____
_____
_____

D. Bob is a lector at his church. His parish community is very friendly and Bob loves being active in church activities, but he doesn't have much time. Since he was once in plays, Bob has a strong voice and he loves to do the readings at Mass. Last Saturday his grandmother came to visit and went to church with Bob. She lives in a retirement center about 20 miles from where Bob lives. After Mass she commented to Bob that she thought her friends would love to have someone read to them like he did. Since they are far away from a town, someone comes out to do liturgies for them only about once a month. Bob knows he really does not have enough extra time. What three things should Bob do?

## GROUP DYNAMIC FUNCTIONS

List the seven group functions. Then make a note when you see one of the group members use one of them:

_____
_____
_____
_____
_____
_____
_____
_____
_____
_____
_____
_____
_____
_____
_____
_____
_____
_____
_____
_____

## GROUP FUNCTIONS (CONTINUED)

## GROUP FUNCTIONS (CONTINUED)

**Commitments**

*Chapter*
**3**

## DEFINING COMMITMENT

**Questions for Discussion**

1. Are you committed to anything or anyone or any group?

2. What does it mean to be committed to something or someone or a group?

3. How does being committed to something or someone or some group change the way a person acts or change the way a person lives life?

4. What is your group's definition of "Commitment"?

The definition of commitment we will be using in this class is:

**COMMITMENT IS**

_____

_____

_____

_____

_____

_____

_____

_____

Make a list of your seven most prized possessions.

_____ 1. _____

_____ 2. _____

_____ 3. _____

_____ 4. _____

_____ 5. _____

_____ 6. _____

_____ 7. _____

Now put a star or check mark in front of the possessions you would have the most difficulty giving up.

**Questions for Discussion**

1. What would your life be like without those starred possessions?

3. What would cause you to give up your most prized possession?

2. Why would it be so difficult for you to give up those favorite possessions?

## THE BIBLE ON COMMITMENT

### Deuteronomy 30:15-20

"Here, then I have today set before you life and prosperity, death and doom. If you obey the commandments of the Lord, your God, which I enjoin on you today, loving him, and walking in his ways, and keeping his commandments, statutes and decrees, you will live and grow numerous, and the Lord, your God, will bless you in the land you are entering to occupy. If, however, you turn away your hearts and will not listen, but are led astray and adore and serve other gods, I tell you now that you will certainly perish; you will not have a long life on the land which you are crossing the Jordan to enter and occupy. I call heaven and earth today to witness against you: I have set before you life and death, the blessing and the curse. Choose life, then, that you and your descendants may live, by loving the Lord, your God, heeding his voice, and holding fast to him. For that will mean life for you, a long life for you to live on the land which the Lord swore he would give to your fathers Abraham, Isaac and Jacob."

## JESUS ON COMMITMENT

### Matthew 13:44-46 The Treasure And The Pearl

"The reign of God is like a buried treasure which a man found in a field. He hid it again, and rejoicing at his find went and sold all he had and bought that field. Or again, the kingdom of heaven is like a merchant's search for fine pearls. When he found one really valuable pearl, he went back and put up for sale all that he had and bought it."

### Matthew 19:16-30 The Rich Young Man

Another time a man came up to him and said, "Teacher, what good must I do to possess everlasting life?" He answered, "Why do you question me about what is good? There is One who is good. If you wish to enter into life keep the commandments." "Which ones?" he asked. Jesus replied, " 'You shall not kill'; 'You shall not commit adultery'; 'You shall not steal'; 'You shall not bear false witness'; 'Honor your father and your mother'; and 'Love your neighbor as yourself.' " The young man said to him, "I have kept all these; what do I need to do further?" Jesus told him, "If you seek perfection, go sell your possessions, and give to the poor. You will then have treasure in heaven. Afterward, come back and follow me." Hearing these words, the young man went away sad, for his possessions were many.

Jesus said to his disciples: "I assure you, only with difficulty will a rich man enter into the Kingdom of God. I repeat what I said: it is easier for a camel to pass through a needle's eye than for a rich man to enter the Kingdom of God." When the disciples heard this they were completely overwhelmed, and exclaimed, "Then who can be saved?" Jesus looked at them and said, "For man it is impossible; but for God all things are possible." Then it was Peter's turn to say to him: "Here we have put everything aside to follow you. What can we expect from it?" Jesus said to them: "I give you my solemn word, in the new age when the Son of Man takes his seat upon a throne befitting his glory, you who have followed me shall likewise take your places on twelve thrones to judge the twelve tribes of Israel. Moreover, everyone who has given up home, brothers or sisters, father or mother, wife or children or property for my sake will receive many times as much and inherit everlasting life. Many who are first shall come last, and the last shall come first."

## SUMMARY AND CONCLUSIONS

From the story of the rich young man we pick up the idea that living in close relationship with God means having the same attitudes toward life that we believe

God has. What seems to be most important to God is love in all its forms. God seems to be committed to relationship with us. God appears to call us to make a decision to be committed to love—love of God, love of others and love of ourselves.

In the gospels we find Jesus to be very committed to his relationship with God. Jesus has great faith in God's love for him and follows a course of action which responds to that love. The gospel writers present Jesus both as God's man and as God's son. As God's man Jesus lives his life in commitment to God. As God's son Jesus calls us to a commitment to God and a way of life that leads to eternal happiness.

Jesus often teaches about commitment to relationship with others. That commitment involves effort at understanding and forgiveness. According to the gospels the most important commitment in life is a commitment to God in and through a commitment to "our neighbor." In his teaching Jesus turns upside down the value system of the world. The greatest treasure is not material possessions it is faith and trust in God in a relationship of love.

We said commitment is the state of being bound emotionally or intellectually to a course of action. Christianity presents us with a course of action quite contrary to what we naturally think is smart according to our world's value system. Christianity calls us to a commitment to interdependence rather than self reliance. Christianity calls us to commitment to Christ in and through the community we call church and which Saint Paul says is the body of Christ.

In any commitment we do not always get back what we want. In God's commitment to us God does not always get back love from us. God is still committed to us, though, and very patient. God seems to want a return commitment on our part, but we are all free and the decision is up to us. Think about it.

## FREE EXCHANGE QUESTIONS

1. What is one of the funniest things that you have ever seen?

2. When have you ever been really scared?

3. If you could wish one thing for your parents what would you wish them?

4. What are two things you want to do in your lifetime?

5. What is your favorite animal? Why?

6. What is your favorite type of car? Why?

7. What, if anything, are you allergic to?

8. Describe the perfect date.

9. What is the most important thing to you in a friendship?

10. How do you react when you lose something?

## REACTION SHEET

1. Over all do you think you gained or lost during this activity? Why?

2. What are your feelings about the things you received?

3. Were you ever upset by what someone else gave you? If so, why? If not, why not?

4. If you had the chance to do this again, would you give things to people differently than you did? If so, how would you do it differently?

5. What things were you most pleased by when you received them? Why?

6. What do you think was the point of this activity?

## JOURNALING—COMMITMENTS

Keeping the person with whom you have the conflict in your mind, journal on your commitment to Christianity.

Try and journal in the form of a conversation either with yourself, with the person you have in your mind or with God.

_____

_____

_____

_____

_____

_____

_____

_____

_____

_____

## JOURNALING CONTINUED

## PRAYER—COMMITMENTS

In the prayer today, group "A" will represent the father in the prodigal son story and group "B" will represent the son who stayed and worked on the farm.

**ALL:** In the name of the Father, and of the Son, and of the Holy Spirit.

**TEACHER:** Dear God, thank you for the mercy you have shown us in our lives. So many times we fall short of the goal of following you, but you are always there to welcome us back when we try to change our ways. It is hard for us to be always consistent. Not living just for ourselves. Being committed to your ways is difficult. Swallowing our pride and accepting what we receive without expectations seems to be nearly impossible. Help us to grow in our commitment to you.

**A:** (Father) My son, you are with me always, and everything I have is yours. But we had to celebrate and rejoice! This brother of yours was dead, and has come back to life. He was lost, and now is found.

**B:** (Other son) It does not seem fair. I try real hard to do what you have asked of me, yet when he returns after doing so many things which were unfair and unjust, he is treated like royalty.

**A:** You are with me always, and everything I have is yours.

**B:** Just once I wish I could get what I want. I wish I could do things my way.

**A:** You are with me always, and everything I have is yours.

**B:** I guess I am selfish about what I expect to get from what I do.

**A:** You are with me always, and everything I have is yours.

**B:** I really don't understand why you have so much compassion and forgiveness. Perhaps my anger is a result of selfishly wanting things my way.

**A:** You are with me always, and everything I have is yours.

**B:** We see the world through different eyes. Mine are clouded with my own desires, ambitions and expectations. It sure takes trust to accept that you are more just and fair than I am.

**A:** You are with me always, and everything I have is yours.

**B:** I can see that because you care for others it does not mean you no longer care for me or that you care for me less. It is truly good to hope for the return of those who do not succeed in their attempts to live life fully. Help me to grow in my commitment to trust you.

**A:** You are with me always, and everything I have is yours.

**READER:** Luke 15:1-7 (paraphrased)
The tax collectors and sinners were all gathering about Jesus to hear him at which the Pharisees and scribes murmured this man welcomes sinners and eats with them. Upon hearing them Jesus addressed this parable to them. Who among you, if he has a hundred sheep and loses one of them does not leave the other ninety-nine and look for the lost one until it is found? And when it is found do you not put it on your shoulders and rejoice telling your friends and neighbors, rejoice with me because I have found my lost sheep. I tell you there will be more rejoicing in heaven over one repentant sinner than over ninety-nine righteous people who have no need to repent.

**ALL:** Merciful God, give us the courage to live a commitment to follow you. Help us to see that our own desires, ambitions and expectations cloud our eyes so we cannot truly see justice clearly. We do not always understand what fair is, especially when fair is not our way. Make our commitment a commitment to giving rather than receiving. Help us to see you as our source of reward.

**ALL:** Our Father . . . (Pray the Our Father)

## ELEMENTS OF COMMUNICATION

**Notes:**

## MISSED COMMUNICATION

Think of a time when you and someone else did not communicate well. This might be the last fight, argument, or discussion, you had with a friend, parent or teacher. Once you have the incident in mind fill in the following information.

Persons involved _____

What was said. (Just the words and ideas)

_____
_____
_____
_____
_____

Different tones of voice used

_____

_____


Body language present during interaction

_____

_____


Environment (Where was this?)

_____

_____


Word choices (Strong or weak words used)

_____

_____


Attitude you had toward the other person and the other person had toward you

_____

_____

_____


Relationship between you and the other person

_____

_____

Did you feel the miscommunication was resolved? Why or why not?

_____

_____

_____


What could be done to avoid this type of miscommunication in the future?

_____

_____

_____

_____

## EFFECTIVE COMMUNICATION

1. Send "I" messages rather than "You" messages. Make sure that you are not expressing your feelings as though they are proven facts.

2. Say something good. Think beyond the current situation and look at what you see as the desired outcome.

3. Stick to the issue. Are you focusing on the issue or are you personally attacking the other person?

4. Talk about what is happening. Where do you want the relationship at the end of this discussion?

5. If things get out of hand call a time out. This does not mean that you quit if you are not winning.

6. Try to express yourself in writing. Focus on where you are coming from.

7. Listen to your self talk. Learn to recognize your own internal signals.

8. Check to see if you are still listening. Do you shut the other person off?

9. Do something unexpected. Be willing to admit having been wrong.

## LISTENING

**STEP 1:**
Let the other person know you are willing to listen. "Door openers," statements which invite the other person to talk with you, are a good initial step. Examples: Is something wrong? Can I help? I'm really interested in how you feel.

**STEP 2:**
The second stage of listening is one most people are fairly familiar with. It is called passive listening and involves just being attentive while the person talks. Passive listening requires keeping quiet while the other person is talking.

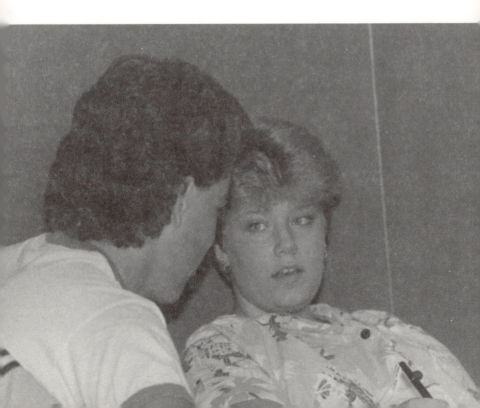

### STEP 3:
Pure passive listening does not let the speaker know that you are aware of what is being said. Some people can look right at you while you are talking and you are sure they are a million miles away. So the third step is acknowledging that you are paying attention.

### STEP 4:
Step four involves the most active participation in the listening process. It is called active listening, because while listening to the speaker you will reflect back your understanding of what he/she is saying. You need to understand three essential elements of what the speaker is saying. These elements are:
1. The words said
2. The feelings expressed
3. The meaning or intention of the feelings and words

## WE ALL HAVE LIMITS

A friend tells you that she thinks she is pregnant and wants to know if she should get an abortion.

Willingness   Low--------------------High

Skill         Low--------------------High

Someone in your class that you like is failing his math class. He wants you to help him study.

Willingness   Low--------------------High

Skill         Low--------------------High

A friend wants to try out for the track team. She is very talented and wants you to help coach her.

Willingness   Low--------------------High

Skill         Low--------------------High

One of the people in your neighborhood says that he has thought about suicide. He has even figured out a way to do it.

Willingness   Low--------------------High

Skill         Low--------------------High

A friend of yours is having a terrible time figuring out how to do a research paper. She is unorganized and is getting very frustrated. She asks if you can help her.

Willingness   Low--------------------High

Skill         Low--------------------High

## Fear of Failure

*Chapter*
**4**

## WHAT IS SUCCESS ACTIVITY

The occupation my group has been assigned is:

_____

Plan a step by step program for success for this occupation.

_____
_____
_____
_____
_____
_____
_____
_____
_____
_____
_____
_____

## WHAT IS SUCCESS ACTIVITY

The occupation my group has been assigned is:

_____

How can you tell if someone is a success in this occupation? What is the measure of success in this occupation?

_____

_____

_____

_____

_____

_____

What is important in life for someone in this occupation? How does a successful person in this occupation treat other people?

_____

_____

_____

_____

_____

_____

_____

## WHAT IS FAILURE ACTIVITY

The occupation my group has been assigned is:

_____

Discuss and write out a list of things, that if a person in this occupation did them he/she would become a failure in that occupation.

_____

_____

_____

_____

Discuss and answer the question: If a person fails in his/her occupation is he/she also a failure in life? Why or why not?

_____

_____

_____

_____

Discuss and answer the question: What makes someone a failure in life?

_____

_____

_____

_____

## SUMMARY—PART ONE

In our world it seems that success is determined by the possessions, wealth or fame a person has. Usually we gain wealth or fame through our occupations. But is that the only way to find happiness and meaning in life? Actually, what brings us the most happiness in life—but also causes the most fear—is our relationships. We want to be in relationship with other people and we fear being rejected and alone. We could have all the possessions we could ever want and all the fame in the world and still be unhappy and lonely. It's only in relationship with others that we can find meaning in life.

The problem is we believe that worldly success, fame and wealth, will get us friends. We seem to equate the two. We think that unless we are beautiful people with all kinds of things going for us and all kinds of desirable possessions no one will want to be around, let alone truly love us. In reality, however, it isn't what we have, but who we are that makes us lovable. Maybe success isn't what we have but becoming all we can be, becoming loving and lovable individuals.

No one plans to fail in life but a lot of people fail to plan and therefore never achieve success. In the second part of class we will be taking a look at the Christian idea of success and Jesus' plan for being successful.

## JESUS AND FEAR

### Mark 14:32-36 Jesus Prays in the Garden

They went then to a place named Gethsemani. "Sit down here while I pray," he said to his disciples; at the same time he took along with him Peter, James, and John. Then he began to be filled with fear and distress. He said to them, "My heart is filled with sorrow to the point of death. Remain here and stay awake." He advanced a little and fell to the ground, praying that if it were possible this hour might pass him by. He kept saying, "Abba (O Father), you have power to do all things. Take this cup away from me. But let it be as you would have it, not as I."

## JESUS' PLAN FOR SUCCESS

### Luke 12:13-21 Trust in God, Not in Possessions

Someone in the crowd said to him, "Teacher, tell my brother to give me my share of our inheritance." He replied, "Friend, who has set me up as your judge or arbiter?" Then he said to the crowd, "Avoid greed in all its forms. A man may be wealthy, but his possessions do not guarantee him life."

He told them a parable in these words: "There was a rich man who had a good harvest. 'What shall I do?' he asked himself. 'I have no place to store my harvest. I know!' he said. 'I will pull down my grain bins and build larger ones. All my grain and my goods will go there. Then I will say to myself: You have blessings in reserve for years to come. Relax! Eat heartily, drink well. Enjoy yourself.' But God said to him, 'You fool! This very night your life shall be required of you. To whom will all this piled-up wealth of yours go?' That is the way it works with the man who grows rich for himself instead of growing rich in the sight of God."

Let's take a look at how Jesus relates to people. Many places in the gospels we read about Jesus' concern for people. All the healing stories and the miracle stories show Jesus' love for people who need help. Sometimes these are people who are very unloveable and shunned by others. Jesus steps right in and helps by giving them what they need most—love and understanding.

Jesus views each person as special. One of the stories in the gospel according to Mark brings this out.

### Mark 5:25-34 The Woman With a Hemorrhage

A large crowd had gathered around Jesus. There was a woman in the area who had been afflicted with a hemorrhage for a dozen years. She had received treatment at the hands of doctors of every sort and exhausted her savings in the process, yet she got no relief; on the contrary, she only grew worse. She had heard about Jesus and came up behind him in the crowd and put her hand to his cloak. "If I just touch his clothing," she thought, "I shall get well." Immediately her flow of blood dried up and the feeling that she was cured of her affliction ran through her whole body. Jesus was conscious at once that healing power had gone out from him. Wheeling about in the crowd, he began to ask, "Who touched my clothing?" His disciples said to him, "You can see how this crowd hems you in, yet you ask, 'Who touched me?' " Despite this, he kept looking around to see the woman who had done it. Fearful and beginning to tremble now as she realized what had happened, the woman came and fell in front of him and told him the whole truth. He said to her, "Daughter, it is your faith that has cured you. Go in peace and be free of this illness."

**NOTES:**

_____

_____

_____

## Matthew 22:34–40 The Great Commandment

When the Pharisees heard that he had silenced the Sadducees, they assembled in a body; and one of them, a lawyer, in an attempt to trip him up, asked him, "Teacher, which commandment of the law is the greatest?"

Jesus said to him:

"You shall love the Lord your God with your whole heart, with your whole soul, and with all your mind.

"This is the greatest and first commandment. The second is like it:

"You shall love your neighbor as yourself.

"On these two commandments the whole law is based, and the prophets as well."

## SUMMARY AND CONCLUSIONS

Love God with all yourself and love your neighbor as yourself. This sounds a little like the 'Golden Rule" Jesus quotes in another place in the gospel: Treat others as you would like them to treat you. The great commandment also brings in a relationship with God first.

Jesus teaches that we will be sure to succeed in life if we will only love God and love people. Now how does that fit into the real world in which we live—the real world where we find ourselves concerned with the desire for possessions, wealth and fame?—The real world where people constantly hurt each other and where we can be hurt if we aren't careful? How can we trust God when it seems that so many bad things happen to people every day?

Trust—that's just the point Jesus makes. We don't always know why bad things happen to people, although humans in their greed are the cause of a lot of it. We don't understand it. The only way out of it is to trust God. To trust that God loves us and in the big picture of what life is all about God wouldn't do anything to hurt us. That's the hard part—to love and trust God even in the face of the ultimate pain and danger, death.

How does Jesus see the value of love fitting into the world that calls us to be concerned about financial security every day? The big question here is your attitude toward wealth and fame.

Your attitude makes the difference—the reason you do something makes the difference. The worldly person is concerned about what he/she can get because that's what's important in life. The worldly person gives because he/she sees a reward in giving. 'I give because I get this in return.' That person starts with the possessions and sees them as bringing happiness, even in relationships.

The Christian person starts with the relationship. He/she gives out of a feeling of love, not to get something. The Christian person is not focused on the reward but on the process. Relationship with God and others is the starting point and the focus. Possessions are not bad; they are useful in helping others and in enjoying life. Possessions are to be shared with others. They are necessary in life, but they are not what's important to happiness and success.

The successful person, the smart person, the happy person according to the Christian system of values may have very few possessions, but does have a great sense of self-worth by loving and being loved by others. Success comes through relationships built on the complete trust that God loves us. The response to that love is in relationships with other people.

The Church is supposed to be the community of people that trust God and lives in a relationship of love with each other. The Church is supposed to be the sign of God's love in the world today.

The Church recognizes the value of all people as being equal, even the ugly, unwanted people in the world. The Church's highest value is the dignity of all life, especially human life, because we believe God loves and is present in all people and all creation.

The reward in following Christ as a member of your Church is an internal reward. You feel good about yourself deep inside because you are responding in love to God's love for you. Following Christ is its own reward, its own success. You know that. You've felt that success each time you've gone out of your way or risked rejection to help a person in need. Maybe it was someone at school, someone nobody else took time for. Maybe it was a member of your family who needed you for awhile. Maybe it was just the time you took to be with a friend who was feeling down. God was present in that love and acting through you. That's success!

As a member of the Christian Catholic Church, what is your commitment to success in life? Think about it.

**Optional Activity**

Write your own Christian plan for success in life.

_____

_____

_____

_____

_____

What are the steps you as a high school student should take to be a success in life?

_____

_____

_____

What are the things you should begin doing tomorrow as the first step to success?

_____

_____

_____

Who are the people you should relate to within the next few days. Why?

_____

_____

_____

What should you begin doing tomorrow in order to form a closer relationship with God?

_____

_____

## MAKE IT OR BREAK IT

Write down some of your mistakes, goof-ups, and failures. You will not have to share any of the ones which you find too embarrassing.

_____

_____

_____

_____

_____

_____

_____

_____

_____

_____

_____

_____

_____

_____

_____

## SOMETIMES I'M AFRAID

Complete each of the following phrases.

Sometimes I'm afraid my parents . . .

Sometimes I'm afraid that in school . . .

Sometimes I'm afraid my friends . . .

Sometimes I'm afraid that in the future . . .

Sometimes I'm afraid God . . .

Sometimes I'm afraid I will . . .

Sometimes I'm afraid . . .

# CREATIVITY

1. Use only four straight lines.
2. Do not lift your pencil from the paper.
3. Connect all nine dots.

★   ★   ★

★   ★   ★

★   ★   ★

**Notes on creativity:**

_____

_____

_____

_____

_____

_____

### Psalm 23:1-6

The Lord is my shepherd; I shall not want.
In verdant pastures he gives me repose;
Beside restful waters he leads me;
he refreshes my soul.
He guides me in right paths
for his name's sake.
Even though I walk in the dark valley
I fear no evil; for you are at my side
With your rod and your staff
that give me courage.

You spread the table before me
in the sight of my foes;
You anoint my head with oil;
my cup overflows.
Only goodness and kindness follow me
all the days of my life;
And I shall dwell in the house of the Lord
for years to come.

### If At First You Don't Succeed
### Mark 8:22-25 (Paraphrased)

When Jesus and his disciples arrived at Bethsaida some people brought to Jesus a blind man and begged him to touch him. Jesus took the blind man's hand and led him outside of the village. Putting spittle on the blind man's eyes, Jesus laid his hands on the man and asked him, "Can you see anything?" The man opened his eyes and said, "I can see people but they look like walking trees!" Then Jesus laid his hands on the man's eyes a second time and he saw perfectly; his sight was restored and he could see everything clearly.

## JOURNALING—FEAR

Refer back to your responses to, "Sometimes I'm Afraid." Journal about one of those fears.

## JOURNALING (CONTINUED)

## PRAYER—FEAR OF FAILURE

**All:** In the name of the Father, and of the Son and of the Holy Spirit.

**TEACHER:** Loving God, You know all of our failures yet you have not forsaken us. Thank you for the love you give us even in our times of doubt and despair.

**ALL:** It is difficult for us to understand how you could care for us even when we fail to live up to our relationship to you. Help us to develop the trust of children to see in a new and creative way how we can live in love with you.

**READER #1:** Romans 7:15-25
I cannot even understand my own actions. I do not do what I want to do but do what I hate. When I act against my own will, by that very fact I agree the law is good. This indicates that it is not I who do it but sin which resides within me. I know that no good dwells in me, that is, in my flesh; the desire to do right is there, but not the power. What happens is that I do, not the good I will to do, but the evil I do not intend. But if I do what is against my will it is not I who do it but sin which dwells in me. This means that even though I want to do what is right, a law that leads to wrongdoing is always ready at hand. My inner self agrees with the law of God, but I see in my body's members another law at war with the law of my mind; this makes me the prisoner of the law of sin in my members. What a wretched man I am! Who can free me from this body under the power of death? All praise to God, through Jesus Christ our Lord! So with my mind I serve the law of God but with my flesh the law of sin.

**ALL:** We are afraid to fail at so many things. Help us to find comfort in the words of your servant Paul who, like us, struggled to do what is right. He found that even when he tried there were times when he did not succeed. Give us the courage to face the fears and shortcomings we have without becoming disheartened. Your Son Jesus touched the lives of many . To those who were paralyzed he gave freedom to move about. Touch our hearts when we become paralyzed by the fear of failing. Help us to reach behind our narrow vision to put our trust in you.

**READER #2:** Matthew 7:24-27
Anyone who hears my words and puts them into practice is like the wise man who built his house on rock. When the rainy season set in, the torrents came and the winds blew and buffeted his house. It did not collapse; it had been solidly set on rock. Anyone who hears my words but does not put them into practice is like the foolish man who built his house on sandy ground. The rains fell and the winds blew and lashed against his house. It collapsed under all this and was completely ruined.

**TEACHER:** God, you are a rock to hold onto even in the worst storms of our lives. Give us the courage to trust you and recognize that depending on you is our greatest strength in times of failure and fear. Help us to swallow our pride and let you know our prayers and our needs.

Open prayer for anyone.

**TEACHER:** Hear our prayers, those we have shared here and those which are deep in our hearts. Give us the courage to trust in you, for you are indeed the rock on which we should build our lives.

**ALL:** Our Father . . .

**NOTES:**

_____

_____

_____

_____

## BLAHS BLUES AND DEPRESSION

### The Blahs
The "blahs" is a mild, short-term depression, usually associated with concrete, external incidents. The blahs are characterized by a general sense of dissatisfaction, and irritability.

### The Blues
The blues also are a mild form of short-term depression, although they tend to last somewhat longer than the blahs. The blues is a feeling usually not associated with any specific, external incident. Rather it tends to be internal and often the cause is not known. The blues are characterized by quiet, withdrawn, introspective behavior. Past a week, though, this type of mood is considered to be a sign of deeper depression.

## Depression

Depression occurs in a severe form only once in awhile. Uncontrolled depression can lead to suicide. Depression is similar to the blahs in that it is usually related to some specific event. The difference is that in depression the event often has both internal and external consequences. Depression is characterized by difficulty in concentration, restlessness, fatigue, acting out, a change in eating or sleeping habits, and a disinterest in usual friends and activities.
Depression can last for long periods of time. Occasionally it can take a year or more to overcome depression.

So I say to you, ask and you shall receive; seek and you shall find; knock and the door shall be opened to you.

For anyone that asks, receives: anyone that seeks, finds; anyone that knocks is admitted.

**John 16:33**

I tell you all this that in me you may find peace.
You will suffer in the world
But take courage!
I have overcome the world.

## DEFEATING DEPRESSION

**STEP 1** Decide you want to get better. How could you help someone make this decision?

_____

_____

**STEP 2** Identify the problem. How could you help a friend identify what the problem is?

_____

_____

**STEP 3** Look for rewards to make things better. Do something positive. What positive things could you do to reward and support a friend?

_____

_____

**STEP 4** Set short and long term goals. What short and long term goals could you suggest for your friend?

_____

_____

**STEP 5** Work on building constructive relationships. What are some ways that you could help a friend build constructive relationships?

_____

_____

## THE QUESTION

Is there a reason to choose living over dying?

State your belief about why you feel life is worth living. What are your reasons why it is good to be alive?

_____

_____

_____

_____

_____

_____

_____

_____

_____

_____

_____

_____

_____

_____

_____

# SUICIDE

### The Signs

The following are signs of depression and suicide. Combinations of these signs, along with exceptional severity of any one of them should be considered danger signals.

1. Changes in eating or sleeping habits
2. Difficulty in concentration
3. Decreased school performance
4. Preoccupation with death or dying
5. Talking about suicide, even jokingly
6. Giving away prized possessions
7. Withdrawal from friends or usual activities
8. Disruptive behavior (excessive substance abuse, outbursts of temper)
9. Reaction to loss of relative, friend, parent, or boyfriend or girlfriend
10. Previous suicide attempts or history of suicide in family

### How to Help

#### STEP 1

If a number of the danger signs are present in a friend, but he/she has not said anything about suicide, you may want to initiate a conversation with your friend. Let your friend know that you really like him/her and that you are available if he/she ever wants to talk. You may want to mention that you have noticed your friend seems more moody or down than usual. Ask if there is something wrong. Communicate that you really care and you are willing to listen if your friend wants to talk. Let the person feel that they are important to you.

#### STEP 2

If your friend has mentioned suicide, even jokingly, take this seriously. (If it turns out that the intent has not been serious, he/she should learn that suicide is not a topic to joke about!) The key to this step is to listen. Listen not only to words but to the nonverbal communication. Explore feelings about death and the person's desire to end life. It is important that you do not turn your back on this friend. Don't reject him/her. What the person wants to know is whether you will understand what has upset them. Give your friend a chance to communicate these feelings.

### STEP 3

Assess the problem. This will occur while you are listening to your friend. Is he/she thinking about suicide? You may even want to ask the question directly, if your friend is not being very clear about his/her thoughts or feelings. If your friend mentions having thought about or attempted suicide in the past, find out what the person feels about suicide now. Look for veiled references to dying such as "wishing I could just go to sleep and never wake up," "want to end it all," "make everything go away." To help you assess the level of seriousness, here is a five level assessment scale.

1. Bothered about something
2. Lacking hope, powerless feeling
3. Thinking about suicide
4. Thinking about methods of suicide
5. Having a plan to carry out suicide.

Anything beyond level one should be considered serious. The higher the level, the greater the seriousness. If a friend describes a method or shows you a weapon you should act immediately. Even in the most depressed moment, a suicidal person desperately hopes someone will help him/her to live.

### STEP 4

Act. Do something. Don't just listen and then walk away. If your friend is anywhere beyond stage one, it is time to get some help. Your friend still needs your support, but he/she also needs the help of a trained adult. You are not a psychologist, but you are a friend. Ask your friend to talk with an adult you both trust. This is not the time for having just between you and me secrets. If you take no action and your friend does commit suicide, you may be facing a great deal of guilt.

## CONFIDENCES

1. Don't sign blank checks.

2. If you feel torn, weigh the possible consequences of not getting others involved.

3. Always take problems to someone with more skill than you. Don't take a friend's confidence to another friend.

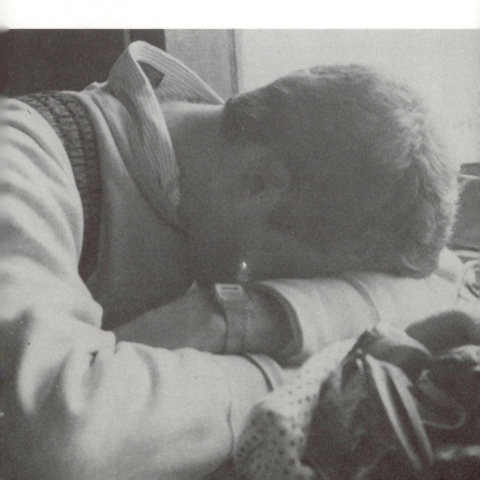

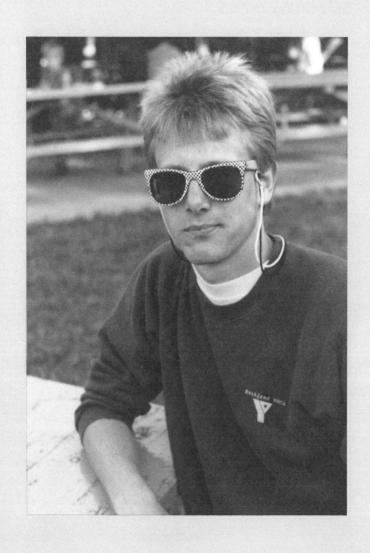

**Peer Pressure**

*Chapter*
**5**

## PRESSURES ON TEENS

In your group come up with a list of at least 20 examples of pressure a teen might feel. Write your ideas to the right of the numbers.

_____ 1. _____

_____ 2. _____

_____ 3. _____

_____ 4. _____

_____ 5. _____

_____ 6. _____

_____ 7. _____

_____ 8. _____

_____ 9. _____

_____ 10. _____

_____ 11. _____

_____ 12. _____

_____ 13. _____

_____ 14. _____

____15. _____

____16. _____

____17. _____

____18. _____

____19. _____

____20. _____

E = an outside pressure (external)
P = an internal or peer pressure
B = both—could be either E or P depending on situation

A peer is an equal—a friend—someone you would like to be like.

**Peer Pressure Is:**

# JESUS AND PEER PRESSURE

## The Blind Bartimaeus (Mark 10:46-52)

They came to Jericho next and as he was leaving that place with his disciples and a sizable crowd, there was a blind beggar Bartimaeus ("son of Timaeus") sitting by the roadside. On hearing that it was Jesus of Nazareth, he began to call out, "Jesus, Son of David, have pity on me!" Many people were scolding him to make him keep quiet, but he shouted all the louder, "Son of David, have pity on me!" Then Jesus stopped and said, "Call him over." So they called the blind man over, telling him as they did so, "You have nothing to fear from him! Get up! He is calling you!" He threw aside his cloak, jumped up and came to Jesus. Jesus asked him, "What do you want me to do for you?" "Rabboni," the blind man said, "I want to see," Jesus said in reply, "Be on your way. Your faith has healed you." Immediately he received his sight and started to follow him up the road.

**NOTES:**

**The Blind Bartimaeus**

**NOTES:**

_____
_____
_____
_____
_____
_____
_____
_____
_____
_____

## CONFORMITY, COMPLIANCE AND ACCEPTANCE

The following letter appeared in the Dear Abby newspaper column.

Pretend you are the author of the Dear Abby column and write an answer to the letter.

DEAR ABBY:

I hope you can offer a practical solution to me and millions of other fathers who face the following dilemma:

A son, about to be married, invites his father to his bachelor party that takes place the night before the wedding. In this day and age, it seems that an X-rated, sexually explicit film is shown as part of the program. Fathers and prospective fathers-in-law are invited to attend, along with the bridegroom and his male friends.

How can a male parent who really doesn't want to attend this kind of party decline without making himself appear prudish or square? Or, if he does attend in order to be accepted as "one of the boys," what is the proper conduct at such parties?

OKIE FROM MUSKOGEE

Write your answer here:

_____

_____

_____

_____

_____

_____

_____

_____

_____

_____

## OH BOTHER CHART!

**Indicate on the Chart How Much Each of These Situations Bothers You!**

1. Asking someone to go out with you and getting turned down.

   0   1   2   3   4   5   6

2. Having someone make fun of you.

   0   1   2   3   4   5   6

3. Knowing that there's a party and you're not invited.

   0   1   2   3   4   5   6

4. Failing at what you are trying to do.

   0   1   2   3   4   5   6

5. Not being asked out on a date.

   0   1   2   3   4   5   6

6. Being rejected by friends.

   0   1   2   3   4   5   6

7. Not being part of the "in group".

   0   1   2   3   4   5   6

8. Looking stupid to other people.

   0   1   2   3   4   5   6

9. Being corrected by your parents or a teacher in front of your friends.

   0   1   2   3   4   5   6

10. Having to go to church on Sunday.

    0   1   2   3   4   5   6

## THE FIVE STEPS:

Take charge of the peer pressure that influences you.

If you are tired of others making your decisions for you and want to escape from a lot of the peer pressure you are feeling here are five steps that will help.

1. Discuss your feelings of pressure with your friends.

2. Find a mentor.

3. Write some goals.

4. Discover what/who influences you.

5. Ask God for help in making a decision to take charge of your life.

## THE INFLUENCE TEST

Think about each of the areas of your life on the list below. On the line provided place the letter of the one or two influences that you most often listen to in making up your mind on the subject.

### INFLUENCES:

A = T.V.    B = The Bible    C = My friends
D = My parents    E = School    F = Church
G = My own ideas

### THE SUBJECTS:

1. \_\_\_\_ Which movies to watch

2. \_\_\_\_ What music to listen to

3. \_\_\_\_ What kind of shoes to wear

4. \_\_\_\_ What hair style to choose

5. \_\_\_\_ What to do in your free time

6. \_\_\_\_ Which T.V. programs to watch

7. \_\_\_\_ What kind of clothes to wear

8. \_\_\_\_ Where to "hang out"

9. \_\_\_\_ What to like and not like

10. \_\_\_\_ What foods to eat

11. \_\_\_\_ What values to hold

12. \_\_\_\_ What moral beliefs to hold

13. \_\_\_\_ What friends to have

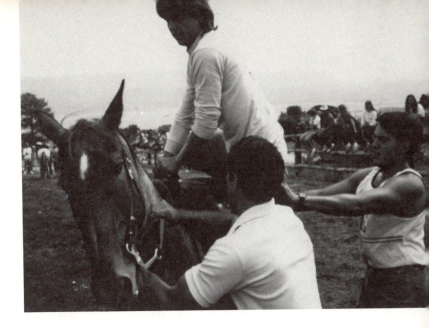

14. _____ Who to want to be seen with

15. _____ What religious beliefs to hold

16. _____ How to act most of the time

## DECISION TO BELIEVE

1. I believe that people are basically good.
                   F  C  P  E  S
2. I believe I am basically a good person.
                   F  C  P  E  S
3. I believe that there is a God who loves us.
                   F  C  P  E  S
4. I believe that if people knew me they would like me.
                   F  C  P  E  S
5. I believe that God answers prayers.
                   F  C  P  E  S
6. I believe that Jesus was the son of God.
                   F  C  P  E  S

7. I believe that if given the chance people will be honest.
   F  C  P  E  S
8. I believe it is better to give than to receive.
   F  C  P  E  S
9. I believe capital punishment is just.
   F  C  P  E  S
10. I believe it is okay to have premarital sex.
    F  C  P  E  S
11. I believe it is okay to have premarital sex if you are in love.
    F  C  P  E  S
12. I believe God forgives sins.
    F  C  P  E  S
13. I believe in heaven and hell.
    F  C  P  E  S
14. I believe my parents love me.
    F  C  P  E  S
15. I believe my friends care about me.
    F  C  P  E  S
16. I believe I make a difference in the world.
    F  C  P  E  S
17. I believe life is worth living even when things are tough.
    F  C  P  E  S
18. I believe a relationship to God is important.
    F  C  P  E  S
19. I believe there is life after death.
    F  C  P  E  S
20. I believe I am loved.
    F  C  P  E  S

## WISDOM OR FOOLISHNESS

1 Cor. 13:4–7

"Love is patient; love is kind. Love is not jealous, it does not put on airs, it is not snobbish. Love is never rude, it is not self-seeking, it is not prone to anger; neither does it brood over injuries. Love does not rejoice in what is wrong but rejoices with the truth. there is no limit to love's forbearance, to its trust, its hope, its power to endure."

The following descriptions of love can be gathered from this reading:

1. Patient
2. Kind
3. Not jealous
4. Not snobbish
5. Never rude
6. Not self-seeking
7. Not easily angered
8. Does not dwell on injuries
9. Rejoices in the truth

## PEER PRESSURE AND THE FIRST FOLLOWERS

### Matthew 26:69-75

"Peter was sitting in the courtyard when one of the serving girls came over to him and said, 'You too were with Jesus the Galilean.' He denied it in front of everyone: 'I do not know what you are talking about!' When he went out to the gate another girl saw him and said to those nearby, 'This man was with Jesus the Nazarene.' Again he denied it with an oath: 'I do not even know the man!' A little while later some bystanders came over to Peter and said, 'You are certainly one of them! Even your accent gives you away!' At that he began cursing and swore, 'I do not even know the man!' Just then a cock began to crow and Peter remembered the prediction Jesus had made: 'Before the cock crows, you will deny me three times.' He went out and began to weep bitterly."

## 5 STEPS TO OVERCOME PEER PRESSURE

1. Discuss your feelings of pressure with your friends.

2. Find a mentor.

3. Write some goals.

4. Discover what/who influences you.

5. Ask God for help in making a decision to take charge of your life.

## JOURNALING—PEER PRESSURE

Reflect on the forces in your life which strengthen your faith and those things which pressure you to abandon or compromise it.

## JOURNALING (CONTINUED)

# JOURNALING (CONTINUED)

_____
_____
_____
_____
_____
_____
_____
_____

## PRAYER—PEER PRESSURE

**All:** In the name of the father and of the Son and of the Holy Spirit.

**Teacher:** Dear God, today we have looked at ways to try to live the values taught by your son. So often we want to do what is right but we stumble and fall, unable to make it on our own. We let the opinions of others change our actions, and we live not to please you but to please those around us.

**All:** Merciful God, forgive us when we lack the courage to live our love for you. We continually act as though what really matters is the opinions of those around us, not our relationship with you. Give us the insight to see that you are with us always, helping us to face the struggles of our lives.

**Reader 1:** John 16:32-33 (paraphrased)

"Do you really believe?
An hour is coming—has indeed already come,
When you will be scattered and each will go his/her way,
leaving me quite alone.
(Yet I can never be alone; God is with me.)
I tell you all this
that in me you may find peace.
You will suffer in the world.
But take courage!
I have overcome the world."

**Teacher:** Help us to understand that you have power over all the earth. Teach us that believing in you is wisdom, not foolishness, and that trusting in you is strength, not weakness. You know the weakness and foolishness of our hearts; grant us strength to seek your wisdom and strength.

**All:** Your love is all around us. There is nowhere we can go that you cannot touch us. Teach us to seek out your ways instead of hiding from them. Help us

to have the courage to respond to your love without fear of what other people will say to us. Even when we feel alone and empty, teach us to see you in all things.

(Optional) Play the song "Be Not Afraid" from the "Glory and Praise" cassette #1.

**Teacher:** Help us to see that you are with us through it all. As we try to open ourselves to you accept our weakness and help us to grow strong in you. Transform our hearts that we might become mirrors of your love, reflecting your light into the darkness of the world around us.

**Reader 2:** Romans 12:2

"Do not conform yourself to this age but be transformed by the renewal of your mind so that you might Judge what is God's will, what is good, pleasing and perfect."

**All:** Dear God, give us the courage to face the pressures of our lives, always holding strong to our faith in you. Your grace will give us the strength needed to begin the renewal of our hearts and our minds. Free us from the prison of conformity that we might joyfully choose you as a guide for our lives.

Pray the "Our father" to conclude the class.

# DRUG AND ALCOHOL GUIDELINES

### Acceptable Use of Drugs and Alcohol

These guidelines should address:

1. How often?
2. Reasons
3. By whom?
4. What affects? (direct and indirect)
5. When and where?

# DRUG AND ALCOHOL GUIDELINES

## Unacceptable Use of Drugs and Alcohol

These guidelines should address:

1. How often?
2. Reasons.
3. By whom?
4. What affects? (direct and indirect)
5. When and where?

# TRUE OR FALSE

In front of each statement place a "T" if you think this is a possible sign of a drug or alcohol problem or an "F" if you think it is not.

    \_\_\_\_ 1. Inappropriate use, such as rapid use, poor timing, etc.
    \_\_\_\_ 2. Using drugs or alcohol alone
    \_\_\_\_ 3. Rejection of concerned people (family)
    \_\_\_\_ 4. Pre-occupation with using chemicals
    \_\_\_\_ 5. Unplanned use of drugs or alcohol
    \_\_\_\_ 6. Decreased school/work performance
    \_\_\_\_ 7. Increased negative relationship with family
    \_\_\_\_ 8. Increased withdrawal from family
    \_\_\_\_ 9. Hospitalization due to chemical use
    \_\_\_\_ 10. Protection of a supply
    \_\_\_\_ 11. Using to feel comfortable in social situations
    \_\_\_\_ 12. Change in values
    \_\_\_\_ 13. Preoccupation with suicide or death
    \_\_\_\_ 14. Feeling uncomfortable when drug abuse is discussed.
    \_\_\_\_ 15. Using with intent to get drunk or stoned
    \_\_\_\_ 16. Changing personal habits such as sleeping or eating
    \_\_\_\_ 17. Legal problems associated with drug or alcohol use
    \_\_\_\_ 18. Personality change such as becoming more passive, withdrawn or irritable
    \_\_\_\_ 19. Skipping school or work
    \_\_\_\_ 20. Memory lapses (blackouts)
    \_\_\_\_ 21. Inability to have fun when sober
    \_\_\_\_ 22. Using drugs or alcohol to deal with feelings
    \_\_\_\_ 23. Feeling guilty about drug or alcohol use
    \_\_\_\_ 24. Changing friends

## IT'S A FREE CHOICE

LEVEL 1: Someone offers alcohol or drugs.

Choice—Based on personal values accept or reject offer. If offer rejected move to level two.

LEVEL 2: Make second offer slightly stronger, adding comment like, "One won't hurt," or "Come on, loosen up a little."

Choice—Based on values and desire to fit in, accept or reject offer. If offer rejected, move to level three.

LEVEL 3: Make third offer, usually much stronger with some put down or insult like, "What's the matter, are you a wimp?" "You some kind of goody-goody or something"? or "Don't be such a baby."

Choice—Based on values, desire to fit in, and security of self image, accept or reject offer. If offer is rejected, sometimes moves to level four.

LEVEL 4: Threaten person refusing to accept offer with some adverse consequences. This usually happens only when drug dealers try to get new customers by coercion. But often the individual who has refused to drink or use drugs with a group will face the adverse consequence of being rejected by that group.

Choice—Based on values, desire to fit in, self image and fear, accept or reject offer. If offer rejected, face adverse consequences.

# RESPONDING IN PRACTICAL WAYS

### Stage one—Experimental use.

In this stage the individual experiments with various types of mood-altering substances. At this point many people decide that chemical use is not for them. While many people do not go beyond experimentation, a great majority become regular users of drugs and alcohol. They seek the mood swings these substances offer.

### Stage two — More regular use.

At this point the reasons why someone is using drugs or alcohol can be seriously questioned. If the user is beginning to lie to others about use of the drugs or alcohol, about who his/her friends are, about why he/she has dropped out of activities, about why a savings account is so low, a sense of guilt may develop. This guilt can lead to feelings of intense self-hatred, which results in increased drug use. At this point the user may begin to display some of the 24 signs and symptoms of chemical dependency in the true false quiz used earlier.

### Stage three—Daily preoccupation

More and more energy, time and money are spent on being high or drunk and insuring that there is an adequate supply. Nearly all of the user's activities are connected to drug use. The user believes that he/she can stop anytime, and problems with parents and police often can lead to short-term abstinence. Generally these periods of abstinence do not last. They do, however, serve to strengthen the user's sincere belief that quitting is no problem. It can be pointed out that while the user feels there is still a choice to use or not to use, the choice is always the same: to keep using.

## Stage four—Dependency

By this stage, the user's negative feelings have reached a state at which they require nearly constant medication with drugs or alcohol. Users are unable to distinguish between normal and intoxicated behavior. Being high is normal, and no amount of argument can break through this chemically maintained delusion. Even when faced with overwhelming evidence the user will insist there is no problem, that he/she is not out of control, and that he/she can quit at any time.

*Chapter*

# Moral Decisions, Part 1

# 6

## MORAL DECISIONS 1

### CARLA AND JOAN

Two young women, who were friends, found themselves in serious trouble. They were secretly leaving town in a hurry and needed money. Carla, wh was a year older than Joan, broke into a store and stole $1,000. Joan, the younger one, went to a rich old woman who was known to help people in the town. Joan told the woman that she was very sick and needed $500 to pay for an operation. (She wasn't sick at all, and she had no intention of paying the woman back.) Although the woman didn't know Joan very well, she loaned her the money. So they skipped town, Joan with the $500 and Carla with $1,000.

1. Which would be worse, stealing like Carla or cheating like Joan? Why?

_____

_____

_____

2. What is so bad about lying to people, in general?

_____

_____

_____

3. Why shouldn't someone steal from a store?

_____

_____

4. What is the basic value or importance of property rights?

5. Which would be worse for the good of society or community, cheating like Joan or stealing like Carla? Why?

6. Would your conscience feel worse if you cheated like Joan or stole like Carla? Why?

7. What do you mean by conscience? What do you think of as your conscience and what does it do?

8. What does the word "morality" mean to you?

Morality is a system of _____

_____
_____
_____
_____
_____

Morality is _____

_____
_____
_____
_____

# AN OUTLINE OF MORAL DECISION MAKING

I  Deliberation
    A. Circumstances
        1. Societal decision
        2. Personal decision
    B. Alternatives
    C. Consequences

II  Judgment
    A. Human Ideal
    B. Christian Ideal

III  Acting According To The Decision

**Notes:**

# THE GREAT COMMANDMENT

Mark 12:28-34

One of the scribes came up and when he heard them arguing he realized how skillfully Jesus answered them. He decided to ask him, "Which is the first of all the commandments?" Jesus replied: "This is the first: 'Hear, O Israel! The Lord of God is Lord alone! Therefore you shall love the Lord your God with all your heart, with all your soul, with all your mind, and with all your strength.'

This is the second, 'You shall love your neighbor as yourself.' There is no other commandment greater than these."

The scribe said to him: "Excellent, Teacher! You are right in saying, 'He is the One, there is no other than he.' Yes, 'to love him with all our heart, with all our thoughts and with all our strength, and to love our neighbor as ourselves' is worth more than any burnt offering or sacrifice."

Jesus approved the insight of this answer and told him, "You are not far from the reign of God." And no one had the courage to ask him any more questions.

**Discussion Notes:**

To be morally good is to make decisions that promote one becoming more fully human and also promote others becoming more fully human.

We learn what Jesus considered to be fully human moral conduct from the Bible and the teachings of the Church.

## THE BASIC TEN

## THE FIRST STEP

**Exodus 20:2-6**

"I, the Lord, am your God, who brought you out of Egypt, that place of slavery. You shall not have other gods besides me. You shall not carve idols for yourselves in the shape of anything in the sky above or on the earth below or in the waters beneath the earth; you shall not bow down before them or worship them. For I, the Lord, your God, am a jealous God, inflicting punishment for their fathers' wickedness on the children of those who hate me, down to the third and fourth generation; but bestowing mercy down to the thousandth generation on the children of those who love me and keep my commandments."

List all the possible distractions you can think of which keep people from living up to the first commandment.

_____

_____

_____

_____

_____

_____

_____

_____

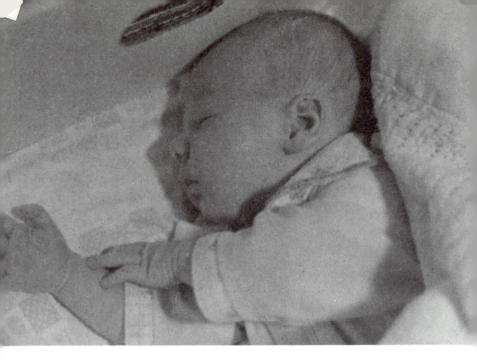

## FIVE TOP PRIORITIES

List the five things in your life which are most important to you. These can be abstract as well as concrete items.

_____

_____

_____

_____

_____

_____

_____

_____

# BALLOON CHRISTIANITY

Matthew 23:24-28

"Blind guides! You strain out the gnat and swallow the camel! Woe to you scribes and Pharisees, you frauds! You cleanse the outside of the cup and dish, and leave the inside filled with loot and lust! Blind Pharisee! First cleanse the inside of the cup so that its outside may be clean. Woe to you scribes and Pharisees, you frauds! You are like whitewashed tombs, beautiful to look at on the outside, but inside full of filth and dead men's bones. Thus you present to view a holy exterior while hypocrisy and evil fill you within."

## JOURNALING—MORALITY

Reflect on the following questions before you begin work in your journal.

1. What priority does God have in your life?

2. What are some of the things in your life which inhibit you from fully accepting God as the top priority in your life?

Now write a letter (to God) which says what you are thinking and feeling about your relationship with God.

_____

_____

_____

_____

## JOURNALING (CONTINUED)

## PRAYER—MORALITY

**ALL:** In the name of the Father, and of the Son and of the Holy spirit.

**TEACHER:** Dear God, it is difficult to be constantly faithful to you. There are so many distractions which keep us from building our relationship with you. Sometimes we let other things replace you as the god in our lives. Teach us to be ever faithful, seeking always to grow in our love for you. You alone are God. Teach us to understand your teachings and live the wisdom of your ways.

**READER 1:** Deuteronomy 6:4–5
"Hear, O Israel! The Lord is our God, the Lord alone! Therefore you shall love the Lord, your God, with all your heart, and with all your soul, and with all your strength."

**ALL:** O God, hear us we pray. Give us the courage and faith to love you with all our heart, soul and strength. Grant us our prayer as we pray in the words your Son taught his first disciples.

**A:** Our Father who art in heaven hallowed be thy name.

**B:** May we always remember that you are above all things. You are all goodness and holiness. Help us remember your love.

**A:** Thy kingdom come, thy will be done, on earth as it is in heaven.

**B:** It is not for us to dictate what has worth in this world. You have set value on all things, especially on us, your creation. We often make mistakes, and frequently err in our ways. Many times we are blind when it comes to choosing how to live morally. Let us always seek your ways for they will always lead us to right decisions. Enter our hearts that we may do your will.

**A:** Give us this day our daily bread.

**B:** You grant us our needs each day, giving us the food we eat and the air we breathe. Help us never to take for granted your constant blessings in our lives.

**A:** Forgive us our trespasses as we forgive those who trespass against us.

**B:** It is hard to admit our mistakes and ask for forgiveness. Sometimes our pride stands before us like a stumbling block. When we are wrong help us to be humble. When others wrong us help us to be merciful and loving, constantly aware of the mercy and love you have shown us.

**A:** Lead us not into temptation but deliver us from evil.

**B:** It is often our fault that we end up in situations where we stray far from your paths. Be always before us leading us in paths of goodness, guiding our decisions that they are always a reflection of your goodness. Save us from the darkness of the world and keep us ever in your care.

**A:** For thine is the kingdom, the power and the glory, now and forever. Amen.

**B:** You, dear God, are all things. With you there is life in your heavenly kingdom. From you comes all power to do right. And to you goes all glory, for you alone are God. You alone are worthy of praise.

**ALL:** As we try to make decisions about life, guide us by the truths you have revealed that we may always be a witness of your goodness, so one day all people will stand together and say you alone are God, there is no other besides you.

# PARENT AND I INVENTORY

Put a "1" if it is seldom true.

Put a "2" if it is sometimes true.

Put a "3" if it is nearly always true.

\_\_\_\_ I tell my parents the whole truth.

\_\_\_\_ My parents trust me.

\_\_\_\_ I think my parents are fair.

\_\_\_\_ I wish my parents would leave me alone.

\_\_\_\_ I tell my parents I love them.

\_\_\_\_ My parents appreciate what I do.

\_\_\_\_ I agree with my parents' values.

\_\_\_\_ If my parents knew what I did when I went out it would not bother them.

\_\_\_\_ I understand and accept the problems my parents face.

\_\_\_\_ My parents tell me they love me.

\_\_\_\_ My parents and I rarely fight about money.

\_\_\_\_ I appreciate what my parents do.

\_\_\_\_ I try to talk to my parents when I have trouble.

\_\_\_\_ My parents approve of my friends.

\_\_\_\_ I believe my parents understand what I feel.

# DEFINING LEVELS OF RELATIONSHIP

Rough, lukewarm and growing

Level of relationship assigned to group.

_____

_____

_____

_____

_____

_____

_____

_____

_____

# ROLE PLAY SITUATION

Yesterday you brought a friend, Bill, to your house to sit around for the afternon. He is a year older than you and you think he is a pretty good guy even though you have known him only for about a month. Today your parents ask you about him. They wonder what kind of a person he is. You don't know him very well but from what you do know he seems to be nice. He always has money to spend and does not make a big deal out of sharing it with people. In passing conversation he mentions that maybe if all things go well he might want you to go skiing with his family when they go on vacation. Some people in your school say that Bill sells drugs and that's why he always has money. You don't know if this is true but you do wonder where he gets his money. You think that your parents may have heard the same rumor so you wonder if this is why they are asking you about him. How would your conversation go?

**NOTES:**

**Moral Decisions, Part 2**

*Chapter*
**7**

## MORAL DECISIONS 2

A dilemma is a situation that requires one to choose between two equally balanced alternatives.

A dilemma is a predicament that seemingly defies a satisfactory solution.

# MORAL DILEMMA ACTIVITY #1

### HEINZ

In Europe a woman was near death from a special kind of cancer. There was one drug that the doctors thought might save her. It was a form of radium that a druggist in the same town had recenty discovered. The drug was expensive to make, but the druggist was charging ten times what the drug cost to make. He paid $200 for the radium and charged $2,000 for a small dose of the drug. The sick woman's husband, Heinz, went to everyone he knew to borrow the money, but he could only get together about $1,000 which is half of what it cost. He told the druggist that his wife was dying and asked him to sell it cheaper or let him pay later. But the druggist said, "No, I discovered the drug and I'm going to make money from it." Should Heinz steal the drug?

After reading the story, answer the question at the end of the story. Besides giving your answer, you must give in detail the reasons you have chosen the answer you did.

### ANSWER:

_____

_____

_____

_____

_____

_____

_____

_____

# MORAL DILEMMA ACTIVITY #2

## JOAN/DEBBIE

Joan is a sophomore in high school. Her parents are very strict and do not let her go to parties at private homes unless they are sure that the party will be well supervised by adults. In fact, Joan's parents do not let her go out very often at all. They feel that Joan should spend most of her time outside of school with the family. Joan likes her family but feels that her parents are too protective and won't let her do anything fun with her friends. She wants to be able to go out more and spend more time with her friends.

Lately Joan has been getting into more and more arguments with her parents about being able to go out more. She especially wants to go to a 16th birthday party for her best friend, Debbie. Debbie and her other friends at school are putting a lot of pressure on Joan to go to this party and Joan knows that one of the guys she really likes a lot will be there too.

Two days before the party Debbie is at Joan's house trying to help Joan convince her mother to let her go to the party. Joan's mother asks Debbie if her parents will be home and chaperoning the party and if there will be any drinking allowed by Debbie at the party. Debbie assures Joan's mother that her parents will be home and that she would never allow any drinking to go on at her party. Joan's mother finally agrees that Joan can go to Debbie's birthday party.

When Joan gets to Debbie's party on Saturday night she discovers that Debbie's parents are not home and that a few of the guys brought along some drinks. When she asks Debbie about her parents she finds out that Debbie knew her parents wouldn't be home and, in fact, her parents don't even know she is having the party. Debbie said that she told Joan's mom the lie so that she would let her go to the party. At the party Joan gets a lot of pressure from her friends to drink. They keep hassling her to at least try it. Finally the guy she likes a lot says that if she just has one small glass of wine they will all quit hassling her. Joan gives in and takes a few sips from one of the drinks and everyone does quit bugging her.

The party is a good time and Joan really enjoyed being with her friends. When she gets home, Joan's mother asks her about the party. Joan says she had a great time and thanks her mother for letting her go. Then her mother asks Joan if Debbie's parents were at the party the whole time and if anyone brought in any drinks. What should Joan do and why should she do that?

**YOUR ANSWER:**

_____

_____

_____

_____

_____

_____

_____

**JOAN/DEBBIE DISCUSSION NOTES:**

1. How do you think Joan is feeling as her mother asks her about the party?

_____

_____

_____

_____

_____

2. Should Joan have left the party as soon as she found out Debbie's parents were not home? How would Joan feel if she left the party early? How would her friends feel about Joan?

_____

_____

_____

_____

_____

3. Do you think Joan's parents are too protective of her? Why or why not? How would you feel if you were one of Joan's parents?

_____

_____

_____

_____

_____

4. Should Joan tell her mother she had a few sips of wine at the party even if her mother doesn't ask if she drank at the party? Why or why not?

_____

_____

_____

_____

_____

5. What do you think about Debbie's friendship with Joan after this incident? How do you think Joan feels about Debbie not telling her mother the truth about the party? Should Joan protect her friend, Debbie? Why or why not?

_____

_____

_____

_____

_____

6. Do you think Joan and Debbie share the same values? Why or why not?

_____

_____

_____

_____

_____

7. Do you think Debbie was being a good friend to Joan in the way she helped Joan get to the party? Why or why not? How do you think Debbie feels about all this now that the party is over?

_____

_____

_____

_____

_____

8. Do you think Debbie has any responsibility to Joan or Joan's mother now that the party is over? Why or why not? How do you think Joan's mother will feel when she finds out Debbie lied to her? What do you think she will do about it?

_____

_____

_____

# DIMENSIONS OF MORAL MATURITY

### UNDERSTANDING:

Understanding might be defined as having an identity with another's situation, feelings and motive.

### CONSISTENCY:

Consistency is conforming to the same principles or course of action in every situation.

# DIMENSIONS OF MORAL MATURITY

### IDENTITY:

Identity means being able to answer the questions: Who am I in relationship to the rest of the world? What makes me me? What makes me different from another person?

_____

_____

_____

_____

_____

### COMMITMENT:

Commitment is a pledge to do something. It is the state of being bound emotionally or intellectually to a course of action.

_____

_____

_____

_____

_____

_____

**MORALITY 2 SUMMARY**

Today we've been discussing morality maturity as something that takes some time to develop in life. All of us every day have to make moral decisions which affect ourselves and others. The moral decisions we make affect how we end up feeling about ourselves. Our decisions also affect our relationships with our friends and our relationship with God. How we act in relationship to others has an affect on our society too. All justice and peace issues are related to how each one of us sees him/herself in relationship to the society and the world.

Becoming a morally mature person involves the dimensions of Understanding, Consistency, Identity, and Commitment as we've discussed them in class today.

As Christians our moral decisions must be based on prayer, study, consultation and an understanding of the teachings of the Church. The community of Church has many years of wisdom behind it in the area of moral behavior. That does not mean that you should blindly follow everything you are taught in religious education classes. If you disagree or question something it is your responsibility to search out the basic teachings of the Church, understand them, and apply them to your life.

And remember that any person can make a mistake when it comes to making moral decisions. Sometimes we can be blinded by the power of sin or misled by the strength of our desire for something. We can make bad moral decisions which hinder our becoming the person God wants us to be. And there are consequences to all our actions both good and bad.

If you do make a mistake in moral decision making and discover negative consequences in your relationship with others and with God, you can admit your mistake, learn from it and, through the sacrament of reconciliation, move toward the goal of becoming the person God wants you to be.

## A DECISION OF CONSCIENCE

**Prayer:**




**Study:**




**Consultation:**




**An understanding of the teachings of the Church:**

## A NEW DILEMMA

Over the weekend the principal of your school had her house vandalized. The vandals broked several windows, slashed the tires of her car, lit off smoke bombs and drove a car around on the lawn tearing up the grass. The police were called in to investigate the incident. You know the people who vandalized the house but you keep quiet because they threaten to turn you in since you have been selling drugs to some of the other kids at school. You might get expelled if you are turned in and that could ruin your chances at getting the job you want. You hear that the police are accusing some of your friends of vandalizing the house. There is circumstantial evidence against them that makes them appear to be guilty. Would you turn in the real vandals?

### INSTRUCTIONS

Use this page and the next page to list how you would inform your conscience in order to make a decision about this moral dilemma. Be as specific as possible.

_____

_____

_____

_____

_____

_____

_____

# A NEW DILEMMA (CONTINUED)

_____
_____
_____
_____
_____
_____

## JOURNALING—MORAL DECISIONS

"My wish for you is similar growth through contact with God. For this purpose, contact with nature and other people can help indirectly, but the special direct means is prayer. Pray and learn to pray! Open your hearts and your consciences to the one who knows you better than you know yourselves. Talk to him! Deepen your knowledge of the word of the living God by reading and meditating on the Scriptures."

John Paul II—"To the Youth of the World"

Reflect on how you use or don't use prayer in your life as part of decision making.

_____

_____

_____

_____

_____

_____

_____

_____

_____

_____

# JOURNALING—MORAL DECISIONS (CONTINUED)

_____
_____
_____
_____
_____

## PRAYER—MORALITY 2

**All:** In the name of the Father, and of the Son, and of the Holy Spirit.

**Teacher:** Holy God, we thank you for all that you give us. Each day you give us opportunities to grow in our relationships with each other and with you. From you all blessings come. You hear our cries and provide for our needs. Though we often stray from you, you never turn away from us.

**A:** Gracious God, you know the foolishness of our ways. You can see our lack of faith and trust. When we feel as though you are not there, give us eyes of faith and endless persistence to seek a way clear to you.

**READING:** Luke 11:5-12 (paraphrased)
Jesus said to them: "If one of you knows someone who comes to you in the middle of the night and says, 'Friend, lend me three loaves of bread. A friend of mine has come to visit and I have nothing to offer him;' and you from inside should reply, 'Leave me alone. The door is shut now and my children and I are in bed. I cannot get up to look after your needs — I tell you, even though you do not get up and take care of the man because of friendship, you will do so because of his persistence, and you will give him as much as he needs.

"So I say to you, ask and you shall receive; seek and you shall find; knock and it shall be opened to you.

"For whoever asks, receives; whoever seeks, finds; whoever knocks, is admitted. What parent among you will give your child a snake if he/she asks for a fish, or hand him/her a scorpion if asked for an egg? If you, with all your sins, know how to give your children good things, how much more will the heavenly Father give the Holy Spirit to those who ask."

**B:** We are often too proud to ask, too lazy to seek, and too frightened to knock. Humble our pride that we might ask for what we need. Enliven our spirit that we might be energized to seek. And soothe our fears that we might have courage to knock.

**All:** God, give us your Holy Spirit, that we may no longer live like people who have no guide. With you and your spirit we have a guide unlike any other. When we face the dilemmas of life we need not fear for you are there beside us. Grant us the grace to always seek our answers in our relationship to you. Strengthen us to remain faithful witnesses to your presence on the earth.

**Teacher:** We also pray for your blessings on our families, our friends, and all those we promised to pray for. We ask for all these things in the words that your son Jesus gave us.

**All:** Pray the "Our Father."

The "Our Father" concludes the class.

## FEELINGS AND FEARS

In your groups write down the *feelings* and the *fears* that someone who has experienced a breakup might feel.

_____

_____

_____

_____

_____

_____

## FINDING THE RIGHT THING TO SAY

In your small groups, write things that you could say or do to help someone through a breakup.

_____

_____

_____

_____

_____

_____

## HELPING OTHERS SURVIVE BREAKUPS

1. Understand the reality of your friend's pain.

2. Help your friend avoid the trap of blaming and judgment.

3. Caution them about jumping into new relationships without thinking.

4. Help your friend see what he/she learned.

5. Find ways to help your friend express his/her feelings.

6. Love him/her.

**Wholeness**

*Chapter*
**8**

## JESUS AND WHOLENESS

### Matthew 4:1-11

Then Jesus was led into the desert by the Spirit to be tempted by the devil. He fasted forty days and forty nights, and afterward was hungry. The tempter approached and said to him, "If you are the Son of God, command these stones to turn into bread." Jesus replied, "Scripture has it: 'Not on bread alone is man to live but on every utterance that comes from the mouth of God.' "

Next the devil took him to the holy city, set him on the parapet of the temple, and said, "If you are the Son of God, throw yourself down. Scripture has it: 'He will bid his angels take care of you; with their hands they will support you that you may never stumble on a stone.' "

Jesus answered him, "Scripture also has it: 'You shall not put the Lord your God to the test.' "

The devil then took him up a very high mountain and displayed before him all the kingdoms of the world in their magnificence, promising, "All these will I bestow on you if you prostrate yourself in homage before me." At this, Jesus said to him, "Away with you, Satan! Scripture has it: 'You shall do homage to the Lord your God; him alone shall you adore.' "

At that the devil left him, and angels came and waited on him.

How does this story show Jesus being concerned about the physical / emotional / intellectual / religious or spiritual needs of himself or another person?

_____

_____

_____

_____

_____

_____

_____

_____

_____

### Matthew 8:1-7, 14-15

When he came down from the mountain, great crowds followed him. Suddenly a leper came forward and did him homage, saying to him, "Sir, if you will to do so, you can cure me." Jesus stretched out his hand and touched him and said, "I do will it. Be cured." Immediately the man's leprosy disappeared. Then Jesus said to him: "See to it that you tell no one. Go and show yourself to the priest and offer the gift Moses prescribed. That should be the proof they need."

As Jesus entered Capernaum, a centurion approached him with this request: "Sir, my serving boy is at home in bed paralyzed, suffering painfully." Jesus said to him, "I will come and cure him."

[Next] Jesus entered Peter's house and found Peter's mother-in-law in bed with a fever. He took her by the hand and the fever left her. She got up at once and began to wait on him.

---

How does this story show Jesus being concerned about the physical / emotional / intellectual / religious or spiritual needs of himself or another person?

**Matthew 12:1-6**

Once on a sabbath Jesus walked through the standing grain. His disciples felt hungry, so they began to pull off the heads of grain and eat them. When the Pharisees spied this, they protested: "See here! Your disciples are doing what is not permitted on the sabbath." He replied: "Have you not read what David did when he and his men were hungry, how he entered God's house and ate the holy bread, a thing forbidden to him and his men or anyone other than priests? Have you not read in the law how the priests on temple duty can break the sabbath rest without incurring guilt? I assure you there is something greater than the temple here.

How does this story show Jesus being concerned about the physical / emotional / intellectual / religious or spiritual needs of himself or another person?

### Matthew 26:36-39

Then Jesus went with them to a place called Gethsemani. He said to his disciples, "Stay here while I go over there and pray." He took along Peter and Zebedee's two sons, and began to experience sorrow and distress. Then he said to them, "My heart is nearly broken with sorrow. Remain here and stay awake with me." He advanced a little and fell prostrate in prayer. "My Father, if it is possible, let this cup pass me by. Still, let it be as you would have it, not as I."

---

How does this story show Jesus being concerned about the physical / emotional / intellectual / religious or spiritual needs of himself or another person?

**Luke 2:41-47**

His parents used to go every year to Jerusalem for the feast of the Passover, and when he was twelve they went up for the celebration as was their custom. As they were returning at the end of the feast, the child Jesus remained behind unknown to his parents. Thinking he was in the party, they continued their journey for a day, looking for him among their relatives and acquaintances.

Not finding him, they returned to Jerusalem in search of him. On the third day they came upon him in the temple sitting in the midst of the teachers, listening to them and asking them questions. All who heard him were amazed at his intelligence and his answers.

How does this story show Jesus being concerned about the physical / emotional / intellectual / religious or spiritual needs of himself or another person?

_____

_____

_____ _____

_____

_____

_____

### Luke 11:1-4

One day he was praying in a certain place. When he had finished, one of his disciples asked him, "Lord, teach us to pray, as John taught his disciples." He said to them, "When you pray, say:

"Father, hallowed by your name, your kingdom come. Give us each day our daily bread. Forgive us our sins for we too forgive all who do us wrong; and subject us not to the trial."

How does this story show Jesus being concerned about the physical / emotional / intellectual / religious or spiritual needs of himself or another person?

_____

_____

_____

_____

_____

_____

### Luke 19:41-44

Coming within sight of the city, he wept over it and said: "If only you had known the path to peace this day; but you have completely lost it from view! Days will come upon you when your enemies encircle you with a rampart, hem you in, and press you hard from every side. They will wipe you out, you and your children within your walls, and leave not a stone on a stone within you, because you failed to recognize the time of your visitation."

How does this story show Jesus being concerned about the physical / emotional / intellectual / religious or spiritual needs of himself or another person?

## John 2:13-17

As the Jewish Passover was near, Jesus went up to Jerusalem. In the temple precincts he came upon people engaged in selling oxen, sheep and doves, and others seated changing coins. He made a [kind of] whip of cords and drove sheep and oxen alike out of the temple area, and knocked over the money-changers' tables, spilling their coins. He told those who were selling doves: "Get them out of here! Stop turning my Father's house into a marketplace!" His disciples recalled the words of Scripture: "Zeal for your house consumes me."

How does this story show Jesus being concerned about the physical / emotional / intellectual / religious or spiritual needs of himself or another person?

## The Church and Wholeness

### Corporal Works of Mercy

(Matthew 25:35-40)
Feed the hungry
Give drink to the thirsty
Clothe the naked
Shelter the homeless
Visit the sick
Ransom the captive
Bury the dead
List ways you can live the Corporal Works of Mercy

_____

_____

_____

_____

_____

_____

_____

_____

_____

_____

_____

**Spiritual Works of Mercy**

Instruct the ignorant
Counsel the doubtful
Admonish sinners
Bear wrongs patiently
Forgive offenses
Comfort the afflicted
Pray for the living and the dead

List ways you can live the spiritual works of mercy

_____

_____

_____

_____

_____

_____

_____

_____

_____

_____

_____

_____

# DIMENSIONS OF WHOLENESS

## Physical

## Intellectual

**Emotional**

**Spiritual**

## THE PARABLE OF THE SILVER PIECES

**(Matthew 25:14-30)**

"A man was going away on a journey. He called in his servants and handed his funds over to them according to each man's abilities. To one he disbursed five thousand silver pieces; to a second, two thousand; and to a third, a thousand. Then he went away. Immediately the man who received the five thousand went to invest it and made another five. In the same way, the man who received the two thousand doubled his figure. The man who received the thousand went off instead and dug a hole in the ground, where he buried his master's money.

After a long absence, the master of those servants came home and settled accounts with them. The man who had received the five thousand came forward bringing the additional five. 'My lord,' he said, 'you let me have five thousand. See, I have made five thousand more.' His master said to him, 'Well done! You are an industrious and reliable servant. Since you were dependable in a small matter I will put you in charge of larger affairs. Come share your master's joy!' The man who had received the two thousand then stepped forward. 'My lord,' he said, 'you entrusted me with two thousand and I have made two thousand more.' His master said to him, 'Cleverly done! You too are an industrious and reliable servant. Since you were dependable in a small matter I will put you in charge of larger affairs. Come, share your master's joy!' Finally the man who had received the thousand stepped forward. 'My lord,' he said, 'I knew you were a hard man. You reap where you did not sow and gather where you did not scatter, so out of fear I went off and buried your thousand silver pieces in the ground. Here is your money back.' His master exclaimed: 'You worthless, lazy lout! You know I reap where I did not sow and gather where I did not scatter. All the more reason to deposit my money with the bankers, so that on my return I could have had it back with interest. You there! Take the thousand away from him and give it to the man with ten thousand. Those who have will get more until they grow rich, while those who have not, will lose even the little that they have. Throw this servant into the darkness outside, where he can wail and grind his teeth.'"

## "TO THE YOUTH OF THE WORLD"

From Pope John Paul II's apostolic letter of March 31, 1985. This letter coincided with the Vatican-sponsored celebration of 1985 as United Nations International Youth Year.

### GROWTH

"Youth should be a process of 'growth' bringing with it the gradual accumulation of all that is true, good and beautiful."

### PHYSICAL

"And so my hope for you young people is that your 'growth in stature and in wisdom' will come about through contact with nature. Make time for this! Do not miss it! Accept too the fatigue and effort that this contact sometimes involves, especially when we wish to attain particularly challenging goals. Such fatigue is creative and also constitutes the element of healthy relaxation which is as necessary as study and work.

"This fatigue and effort have their own place in the Bible, especially in Saint Paul, who compares the whole Christian life to a race in the sports stadium.

"Each one of you needs this fatigue and effort which not only tempers the body but also enables the whole person to experience the joy of self mastery and victory over obstacles and barriers. This is certainly one of the elements of 'growth' that characterize youth."

### EMOTIONAL

"The Apostle writes that you young people are strong in the strength of divine doctrine: the doctrine contained in Christ's Gospel and summed up in the 'Our Father'. Yes! You are strong in this divine teaching, you are strong in this prayer. You are strong because it instills into you love, goodwill, respect for people, for their life, their dignity, their conscience, their beliefs and their rights. If 'you know the Father' you are strong with the power of human brotherhood."

## SPIRITUAL

"Open your hearts and consciences to the one who knows you better than you know yourselves. Talk to Him! Deepen your knowledge of the word of God by reading and meditating on the Scriptures.

"These are the methods and means for coming close to God and making contact with Him. Remember that it is a question of a two-way relationship. God responds also with the most 'free gift of self', a gift which in biblical language is called 'grace'. Strive to live in the grace of God!"

## INTELLECTUAL

"So it is always a question of effort which is creative. This refers not only to study or mental and intellectual work in general but also to the ordinary kinds of physical work that seemingly have nothing 'creative' about them.

"The work which characterizes the period of youth is, above all, a preparation for the work of adulthood, and so is linked to the school. As I write these words to you young people, I am therefore thinking of all the schools all over the world to which your young lives are linked for a number of years.

"However, whenever we discuss the question of education, study learning and school, there emerges a question of fundamental importance for the human person and in a special way for a young person. This is the question of truth. Truth is the light of the human intellect. If the intellect seeks from youth onwards, to know reality in its different dimensions, it does so in order to possess the truth: in order to live the truth. Such is the structure of the human spirit. Hunger for truth is its fundamental aspiration and expression."

## JOURNALING—WHOLENESS

All religion, all life, all art
all expression comes down to this;
to the effort of the human soul
to break through its barrier
of loneliness, of intolerable
loneliness, and make some contact
with another seeking soul, or with
what all souls seek, which is
(by any name) God.
—Don Marquis—

1. Reflect back over what you have learned in the past year. How have you grown?

2. Has your growth been towards a closer relationship with God or towards a more distant relationship?

_____
_____
_____
_____
_____
_____
_____
_____
_____
_____

## JOURNALING—WHOLENESS (CONTINUED)

## JOURNALING—WHOLENESS (CONTINUED)

_____
_____
_____
_____
_____
_____
_____
_____
_____
_____

# WRITE PRAYER SERVICE

**Assigned dimension of wholeness**

_____
_____
_____
_____
_____
_____
_____
_____
_____
_____
_____
_____
_____
_____
_____
_____
_____
_____
_____
_____

## PRAYER—WHOLENESS

**ALL:** In the name of the Father and of the Son and of the Holy Spirit.

**TEACHER:** Dear God, you constantly reach out to us in love, always yearning for us to turn to you. Often we are stubborn and refuse to see what you have done for us. We look at all we have and believe that we have created it. Free us from our pride so we can accept that all that we have is a gift from you. In our selfishness and pride we choose paths which will lead to destruction, guide us in paths of wholeness. You alone are God, live in us all of our days.

**READER 1:** (Romans 14:7-9) paraphrased
None of us lives as our own master. While we live we are responsible to the Lord, and when we die we die as his servants. Both in life and in death we are the Lord's. That is why Christ died and came to life again, that he might be Lord of both the dead and the living.

**ALL:** Merciful God, forgive us when we are self-centered. Guide us as we seek your paths to wholeness.

**PHYSICAL:** (Group assigned physical dimension)

**ALL:** Lord hear our prayer.

**EMOTIONAL:** (Group assigned emotional dimension)

**ALL:** Lord hear our prayer.

**INTELLECTUAL:** (Group assigned intellectual dimension)

**ALL:** Lord hear our prayer.

**SPIRITUAL:** (Group assigned spiritual dimension)

**ALL:** Lord hear our prayer.

**TEACHER:** Grant us our requests and keep us safe until we meet again, we pray all these things in the name of Jesus, your son.

**ALL:** "Our Father . . ." (Pray the "Our Father").

### Mark 4:1-10 and 13-20

"On another occasion he began to teach beside the lake. Such a huge crowd gathered around him that he went and sat in a boat on the water, while the crowd remained on the shore nearby. He began to instruct them at great length, by the use of parables, and in the course of his teaching said: 'Listen carefully to this. A farmer went out sowing. Some of what he sowed landed on the footpath, where the birds came along and ate it. Some of the seed landed on rocky ground where it had little soil; it sprouted immediately because the soil had no depth. Then, when the sun rose and scorched it, it began to wither for lack of roots. Again, some landed among thorns which grew up and choked it off, and there was no yield of grain. Some seed finally landed on good soil and yielded grain that sprang up to produce at a rate of thirty, sixty and a hundredfold.' Having spoken this parable he added: 'Let him who has ears to hear me, hear!'

Now when he was away from the crowd, those present with the twelve questioned him about the parables."

He said to them: 'You do not understand this parable? How then are you going to understand other figures like it? What the sower is sowing is the word. Those on the path are the ones to whom, as soon as they hear the word, Satan comes to carry off what was sown in them. Similarly, those sown on rocky ground are people who on listening to the word accept it joyfully at the outset. Being rootless, they last only a while. When some pressure or persecution overtakes them because of the word, they falter. Those sown among thorns are another class. They have listened to the word, but anxieties over life's demands, and the desire for wealth, and cravings of other sorts come to choke it off; it bears no yield. But those sown on good soil are the ones who listen to the word, take it to heart, and yield at thirty, sixty, and a hundredfold.'

## CLOSING PRAYER

"In the name of the Father and of the Son and of the Holy Spirit.

Dear Lord, open our ears to hear your message of salvation.

Move our hearts that we might accept this message of love.

Loosen our tongues that we might share this wonder with others.

and guide our steps that we might follow you one day at a time,

a witness to your glorious love,

ever nearing you, in this journey of life. Amen."